CRiSSY® Doll

and HER FRIENDS

Guide for Collectors

CRiSSY® Doll
and HER FRIENDS
Guide for Collectors

By Beth Gunther

ANTIQUE TRADER BOOKS

A DIVISION OF
LANDMARK SPECIALTY PUBLICATIONS
NORFOLK, VIRGINIA

ISBN: 0-930625-71-4
Library of Congress Catalog Card Number: 98-71059

Editor: Wendy Chia-Klesch
Copy Editor: Sandra Holcombe
Designer: Heather Ealey

Printed in the United States of America

To order additional copies of this book, or to obtain a catalog, please contact:
Antique Trader Books
P.O. Box 1050
Dubuque, Iowa 52004
or call 1-800-334-7165

Contents

Dedication

For my family:
Thanks for keeping the house clean, Josh; thank you for your honesty, Shannon; thank you, Miles, for being the person you are—and thank you, Kent, for your enormous patience.

Thank you for being my friends, Marcia, Cyndie, Carolyn, Debra, Diane, and Melissa. You know who you are . . . LYLAS.
Always.

Being part of toy history is a major accomplishment indeed. The inventors of Ideal were geniuses, and were known for creating dolls and toys that "do" things. They pioneered the "drink and wet" doll with "Betsy Wetsy." Other examples of their genius are "Giggles," who giggled when her arms were pushed together, "Kissy," who did just that, and "Whoopsie," whose pigtails flew up in the air with a squeeze of her tummy.

Finally in 1969, the Beautiful Crissy® doll debuted. Her softly elegant features made her a best seller. Recognizing the marketing potential of the "grow-hair" concept, Ideal released many other beautifully sculpted dolls with the grow-hair feature during subsequent years, along with tons of accessories. With the exception of Baby Crissy and later issues of Crissy and Velvet released in the 1980s, each of the Ideal girl's hair grew with the touch of a button and a tug on the long ponytail. A simple turn of the knob on the doll's back made the hair retract to a shorter length.

The beautiful artistry of sculptor Neil Estern is awesome. Mr. Estern sculpted most of the Crissy family line. Ideal master sculptor Vincent J. DeFilippo created the Sears Exclusives, Tressy and Cricket, Magic Hair Crissy, and the head of Baby Crissy. The graceful limbs, expressive hands, and the angelic faces are a study in artistic perfection from demure Kerry to impish Mia. If you own one, you'll want to own them all!

This book will help both the doll dealer and the doll collector in many ways. Doll identification, packaged clothing, cases, accessories, and paper products will be presented.

It is hoped that the reader will understand that the prices herein are representative of current pricing trends. For obvious reasons, a mint in the box (MIB) example fetches more than a nude, played with doll; a loose doll, in its original attire, would be priced somewhere in between.

At this time, Crissy and her family are readily available. Some collectors prefer to have one of every issue MIB along with all the clothes and accessories. Some like to purchase nude dolls, style the hair, and dress them up in one of the ultra cool, fabulously mod Ideal outfits. On a personal plane, this collector likes to have one of everything MIB and tons of unboxed gals to wear those fab outfits. And the hair care aspect is tons of fun.

With prices so low at this time, now is the time to search out the Ideal girls. They are the very personification of the groovy 1970's fashion trends. Enjoy!

So much to wear, so little time! Not counting the original issue outfits that came on the dolls, the Big Girls had 33 outfits to choose from! Here are just a few of them.

Chapter 1

The Big Girls

So many dolls have come and gone in toy history, but very few actually have staying power. With the exception of one very popular 11-1/2-inch fashion doll, dolls today do not have clothing lines, accessories, furnishings, cases, friends, and family.

In 1969, Ideal's designers were probably proud of their accomplishment. The Beautiful Crissy® doll had been released and was enjoying quite a measure of success. The mod girl with the incredibly long tresses proved to be so popular, in fact, that Ideal quickly planned and released a series of other dolls who utilized the "grow-hair" concept as well. There were two main sizes of dolls in the "grow-hair" family: the larger, 18-inch Crissy doll and her same-sized friends, and their "younger," 15-inch companions. The larger dolls will be the focus of this chapter.

The collection of larger dolls includes the Crissy doll herself, and her friends Kerry, Tressy, and Brandi. Each doll was created to be a unique individual with a charm all of her own. Although the larger dolls' bodies were all cast in the same molds, giving them all the same shaped bodies, arms, and legs, each was cast in different skin tones and had different hair colors. The dolls' varying facial expressions reveal the range of their personalities, from a shy, Irish lass, to a carefree beach comber. Crissy, Kerry, and Tressy all have gorgeous glassene eyes. Brandi's eyes are painted.

The play theme with these dolls focused on the hair. At first, Crissy did nothing special, except to grow a great head of hair that could be braided, shortened, or styled. But, later, Ideal had her "do" things . . . like twist and turn, talk, and look around as she stood in one spot.

Most of the dolls were available at local toy or department stores. Sometimes the Sears catalogs treated little girls to exclusive sets that included gowns or outfits only available by catalog order. For instance, some Tressys had a wonderful wedding gown included in the box. What a treat for a little girl or boy back then . . . and for collectors today!

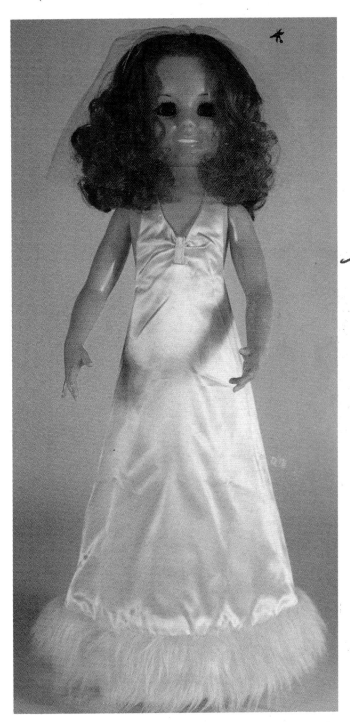

A beautiful Big Girl, Crissy models the hard-to-find "Lemon Lite" (1972).

Interestingly, the collector will find that there are several kinds of knobs (used to retract the ponytail) that appear on the back of the grow-hair doll. For the most part, the earlier the Crissy doll was produced, the more likely she is to have what is called the flower knob. On the later Crissy dolls, the smooth, round knob appears more frequently. However, after the 1969 production year, there seems to be no rhyme nor reason as to which doll would have what kind of knob, flower or smooth. In fact, some later production Crissy dolls—indeed, all of the 18-inch dolls—can appear with either kind of knob. The confusion arises among the smaller family members, too. Early Velvet dolls, as well as Mia, Cricket, and Dina dolls, also appear with both kinds of knobs. Cinnamon has her own style of knob: flush to her back, with small finger tabs.

Also, it is not unusual to find a doll whose knob color does not match her skin tone: The number one Crissy can have the flower knob in white or flesh-colored, regardless of whether she is white or black.

The knobs make it easy to style the dolls' hair in different lengths: "short and sweet" or "long and lovely." To make a Crissy doll's hair grow, push the button on her tummy, and then give her 'tail a tug. Her hair then grows to the desired length. To make her hair short again, turn the knob on the back of the doll, and the 'tail retracts. This is how most of the dolls work, but Baby Crissy and very late-issue Crissy and Velvet dolls operate differently.

Are you ready to take a nostalgic look at the 1970s? Then it is time to come meet Crissy and her friends!

A Bevy of Beauties! Four early Crissy dolls, left to right: 1970 Crissy (hair to waist) in "Grape Drape" (1971); 1969 (hair to feet) black Crissy in original apple green minidress; 1969 white Crissy modeling "The Seventies Satin" (1970); and 1970 Crissy in "The Snuggler" (1971).

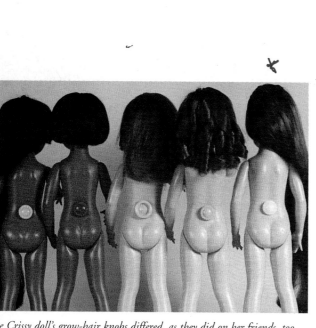

The Crissy doll's grow-hair knobs differed, as they did on her friends, too. Left to right: the black hair-to-the-floor Crissy with a flesh-colored flower knob; black Tressy with a brown flower knob; 1970 Crissy with a round knob; 1970 Crissy with a flower knob; and a number one, hair-to-the-floor Crissy with a white knob.

The Crissy® Doll

The star of the grow-hair show is Beautiful Crissy herself. Debuting in the late 1960s with luscious auburn hair, black pupil-less eyes, and a gorgeous wardrobe, she was an instant hit. The cardboard box that housed the pretty pre-teen was just as interesting as Crissy herself. There is probably not a collector anywhere who would not recognize the hand-drawn profile of Crissy on the early boxes. Later, as other issues were released, the Crissy doll's boxes changed, making every box unique.

Standing in at 18 inches, she is long and leggy. Like the other larger dolls, she has a slightly developing bustline. Her cheeks are lightly blushed, and her carnation pink lips part in a lovely smile showing her white painted "teeth."

Flower Knob —
1970

This aqua minidress is stunning with the 1970 Crissy doll's auburn tresses. (Description on page 13.)

$ 29. 99

11

A product information sheet provided to prospective toy store buyers at the 1969 Toy Fair calls this doll, "'CRISSY' THE HAIR GROWING DOLL 18" Girl Doll with rooted growing hair . . . Pull Crissy's hair and it grows all the way to the floor . . . Turn knob in Crissy's back to rewind long flowing hair." While grammatically challenged, it was an accurate description of the first-issue Crissy doll. Indeed, her hair did grow to her feet, sometimes longer, with this first issue.

This first doll's hair had a tendency to be "woolly" or "nappy," and was difficult to style. Some dolls may be found today with woolly non-growing foundation hair and silky growing hair, or vice versa. Styling concerns with the number one Crissy will be discussed in Chapter 9.

The number one Crissy wears an orange minidress with an orange lace overlay and an orange flocked bow at her upper neckline. Her orange panties match her dress and have white lace trim at the leg openings. Her shoes are also orange, made of soft vinyl. Like all of Crissy's early shoes, they are styled in a low-heeled flat with a molded bow on the toe. The black doll with hair that grows to the floor was issued wearing an apple green version of the same dress, and apple green shoes made in the same style. The bow at her neckline is an unusual pink-flocked ribbon, but it is sometimes found in apple green.

The 1969-issue box is the well-known, previously mentioned profile box with an orange yarn handle. It has three photographs of Crissy, depicting her with her hair extended to various lengths.

Later in 1969, Crissy's hair mysteriously quit growing to her feet. From then on, her hair came only to just below her bottom. Although her dress and stock number remained the same, her box changed slightly, too, reflecting the change in her hair length. New pictures on the box showed her with her new, shorter tresses, and the wording on the box changed from "with hair that grows right down to her toes" to "with hair that grows and grows and grows."

Curiously, a small amount of these Crissy dolls can be found with brownish hair with an auburn cast to it. Her hair is not the true auburn of the typical Crissy doll, nor is she a true brunette, but her hair color falls somewhere in between. She is often called "the brown-haired Crissy." The hair has sometimes turned woolly.

Crissy in 1969: Both black and white issues came with hair to her feet. By the end of the year, her hair only came somewhere between her derriere and her knees. Note the differences in the photos on the boxes.

Avid collectors love to find variations such as this: The Crissy on the left has hair that is significantly more brown than auburn. Some collectors call her the "brown-haired Crissy."

1970: Beautiful Crissy®, stock #1061-1 (white) and #1062-9 (black)

Crissy's stock number changed in 1970. Her hair length, however, remained the same—it still grew only to just below her bottom. Never again would she be issued with hair that grew to her toes.

The white doll released in this production year wears a long-sleeved dress in a lovely shade of aqua. A sash with a metal flower-shaped "buckle" circles her waist and snaps in the back. Her shoes are in the same style as the previous year's, but they are aqua to match her dress, as pictured on page 11. She also wears matching panties trimmed with white lace. The black doll is dressed in the same outfit she modeled in 1969, the apple green lace minidress. Sometimes, though, she wears the new aqua dress, too.

The box for the white doll looks very similar to the 1969-issue box. The only change that occurred between the first two years of Crissy's production was that the three photographs now showed Crissy in her new dress.

The 1970 Ideal catalog shows the black Crissy in her 1969-issue box, which pictures her wearing her apple green dress, in spite of the fact that, as mentioned earlier, she came in two different outfits in 1970.

A highly sought-after black version of Crissy looks fab in her apple green lace minidress. (1969-1970)

1971: Movin' Groovin' Crissy®, stock #1082-7 (black & white)

Crissy was on the move in 1971. Her new swivel waist allowed her to bend and pose, move and groove—the better to model all her hip fashions. The doll's facial features remained the same as they did for most of her issues.

Stepping out in orange boots with molded laces, Movin' Groovin' Crissy definitely looks ready to do just that. She wears an orange jersey mididress belted with orange and brown cords. Her panties are made of matching fabric with white lace at the leg openings.

In 1971, her box sported a new drawing on it. It was no longer the trademark profile of Crissy, but a picture of her from the front. The black doll's box shows her drawn with brown skin and purplish black hair. Movin' Groovin' Crissy's box includes a hairstyling booklet and a rat-tail hairbrush.

New box, new clothes, and a great poseable figure for 1971!

Two Crissy issues were offered in 1971. The Talky
Crissy doll's face was as exquisite as ever, but now she
talked! Her plastic butterfly pullstring comes from her left
hip through a buttonhole on her housecoat. She says
twelve different phrases:

"Hi, I'm Crissy."
"Velvet talks, too."
"Let's have a party!"
"I love you."
"Make my hair long."
"I've got a secret."
"My hair grows!"
"Brush my hair, please."
"Make my hair short."
"I like to dress up!"
"Set my hair, please."
"Please dry my hair."

The Talky Crissy drawn on this doll's box is wearing her first-issue orange lace minidress. Talky Crissy never wore that dress, but she looks comfy in her pink satin housecoat.

The very rare six-phrase Talky Crissy. There is a corresponding six-phrase Talky Velvet in a similar box. (Six-phrase Talky Crissy courtesy of Frank Sposato)

Her hot pink satin housecoat ties with a white corded sash with white pompons on the ends. Her panties match her robe, and she wears pink shoes.

The 1971 box also shows a drawn Crissy doll on the front with three smaller pictures of Crissy in her issue outfit with her hair at different lengths. Enclosed in the box were various hair accessories, including pink curlers, velvet ribbons, yarn hair ties, bobby pins, and a rat-tail hairbrush.

The 1972 and 1973 Talky Crissy boxes were different, in that there was an actual photograph of Crissy dressed in her hot pink housecoat on the front. The Ideal buyer's catalog states that this issue says only six phrases.

The six-phrase Talky Crissy came in this box. Her speaker is situated directly in the middle of her lower belly unlike the twelve-phrase doll whose speaker is placed above her right hip. As mentioned, the twelve-phrase doll has a pullstring coming from her left hip through a hole in her housecoat, but the six-phrase Crissy's is placed on her lower back. Also, one immediately notices that this is the only Crissy doll issue with molded-in nipples. This doll says:

"What did you say?"
"I'll never tell."
"I don't think so."
"Why not?"
"I'll tell you tomorrow."
"That sounds like fun."

This doll and box are very rare.

Talky Crissy and cousin Talky Velvet as they appeared in the 1972 Ideal buyer's catalog. Note that the box is different from the 1971 box.

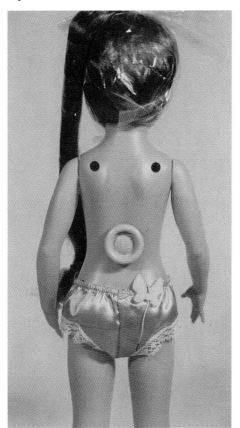
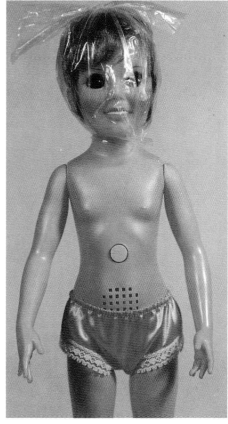

1972: Look Around Crissy®, stock #1092-6 (white) and #1097-5 (black)

Still sporting auburn tresses that extended to below her bottom and black pupil-less eyes, Crissy had a new gimmick in 1972. With the tug of a butterfly pullstring, situated right under the knob on her back, Crissy turned from side to side and "looked around!"

Dressed with a holiday flair in a long, plaid, taffeta dress in rich jewel tones, Look Around Crissy looks beautiful. At her waist, she wears a striped grosgrain ribbon decorated with a silk flower. Her panties are also made of plaid taffeta, and she wears green shoes. The design of Crissy's shoes changed slightly with this issue; they were Mary Jane-styled with a small wedgie heel. Sometimes, the doll appears wearing green shoes similar to the ones she wore in previous issues. The black doll is dressed identically.

The Crissy doll's face is a study in perfection, from her high cheekbones to her smallish nose.

Look Around Crissy looks formal in her jewel-toned taffeta gown. The high ruffled collar helped hide the long neck stem on this issue.

In this beautiful 1973 issue, Crissy looks charming in a dress constructed to look like a jumper over a blouse. In actuality, it is a one-piece dress. On her left shoulder, she dons a plastic and felt corsage. She wears white panties with lace at the leg, and her shoes are in the "new" style, a pair of red-orange wedgie Mary Janes. With this issue, both black and white dolls model the same outfit.

A very unique feature to this doll is the "Swirla-Curler." This device is inserted into the grow hole on the doll's head. Then the little hairdresser divides Crissy's hair into five sections, wrapping each section around one of the five posts of the Swirla-Curler. The result: a head full of luscious curls. Along with new curls for her long, flowing 'tail, Crissy's short foundation hair was also given a new look in 1973. She now sported a slightly different cut with more body and curl.

The box has unusual graphics at the bottom and a small photo of Crissy near the top.

Two Beautiful Crissy dolls at their very best. Finding mint-in-box (MIB) dolls with their hair still factory wrapped is a collector's dream! There is some slight variation in the plaid print on their dresses.

Many times, the back of Crissy's box is the same as the front of the box. When Ideal decided to make the back of the box different, the results were simply charming!

1974: Beautiful Crissy® with Twirly Beads, stock #1210-4 (white) and 1214-6 (black)

The only 1970s issue with different face paint, this Crissy doll has softer, more appealing features. Her eyeliner and painted lashes differ from the first issues', and even her vinyl is softer and of a peachier tone than the earlier Crissy dolls'. Her shorter foundation hair is styled in a layered cut.

She wears a pink and white checked, long, sleeveless dress with eyelet lace at the neckline. She wears plain white panties. Her shoes are the "new" Mary Jane-style in white.

Like the Swirla-Curler, the Twirly Beads hairdo dangle is a unique device that inserts into the grow hole on top of a Crissy doll's head. Once the device is in place, two bendable lengths of white and pink molded beads which are attached to the inserted cone, drape through the doll's hair. Intertwining Crissy's long hair with the beads creates new, mod hair styles.

Crissy gazes into a mirror on the front of this issue's box. We see her reflection staring back at us. It is a lovely photograph of Crissy with her new white and pink Twirly Beads adorning her head. This issue is probably one of the hardest to find.

This country-looking Crissy is hard to find in such good condition.

1977: Magic Hair Crissy®, stock #1280-7 (white) and #1281-5 (black)

The grow-hair concept came to an end momentarily in 1977. Crissy in name only, this doll looks nothing like the earlier Crissy dolls. The only trait she shares in common with her grow-hair predecessor is her auburn hair. She was cheaply made with a very lightweight molded body. While she still had pretty, expressive hands, they were cast in a different mold than before. In fact, her entire body, head, and limbs were made from new, different molds. Still, her face is somewhat pretty, and she has painted blue eyes. The black doll has brown painted eyes and black hair.

Instead of having a ponytail that would grow, this doll was issued with hair pieces that attach with Velcro fasteners. There is a fall, a curly perm style, two sausage curl pigtails, a fantasy style of ribbons, braids and flowers, and two curly braided dangles with white and pink beads on the ends.

Her clothing lacks quality. She wears a shiny pink skirt with lace at the hem. Her top is an eyelet lacy camisole with white ribbon for straps and a silk flower at her waist-line. Her shoes are slide-on mules of white plastic. She wears plain white panties.

Magic Hair Crissy didn't enjoy a huge following in 1977, nor does she now. This may be because she didn't look much like her old self.

1982: Country Fashion Crissy®, stock #1035-5 (white) and #1036-3 (black)

This is Crissy? At first glance, this doll may appear to be grow-hair cousin Velvet (to be discussed later). Indeed, this doll was cast with the Velvet molds, and this made her only 15 inches tall. She still had auburn hair, like always, but her eyes were lavender glassene eyes like Velvet's.

The way Crissy's hair grew in the 1980s was different, too. The mechanics are unlike previous Crissy issues. Her 'tail is about the same length, but is attached to a pull-string on the inside of the doll. As the large plastic ring on her back is pulled, her hair retracts inside. Simply tugging on the 'tail makes it long again.

Her pink, gingham country dress is a one-piece—made to give the illusion of being a jumper and blouse. A perky straw hat perches on top of her head. She wears white knit knee socks and white T-strap Mary Janes styled like cousin Velvet's shoes.

Unfortunately for the collector, well-intentioned doll dealers have a tendency to call this doll "a rare auburn-haired Velvet." An informed buyer will be prepared to tell the difference.

1982-1983: Beautiful Crissy®, stock #1030-6 (white) and #1031-4 (black)

This issue was the same for both years, each having the same box, clothes, hair, eyes, and stock number. Crissy was still made with the older Velvet molds. The only difference between this doll and Country Fashion Crissy is that she wears a white, sleeveless frock, trimmed with pink and white lace, and a pink ribbon sash. She wears the same shoes as Country Fashion Crissy, and her panties are white. Some of these dolls have brown eyes, making them more similar to the earlier Crissy dolls.

1983: Country Fashion Crissy®, stock #10355 (white) and #10363 (black)

Again, we find Crissy looking like all the other 1980s ladies. Her box was the same as the 1982 Country Fashion doll's, but her stock number was now unhyphenated.

The outfit changed from pink gingham in 1982 to lavender gingham in 1983.

Two versions of the 1980s-issued Crissy doll. One wonders why Ideal didn't choose to use the original Crissy molds instead of the Velvet molds.

This Crissy-issue adopted the grow-hair mechanism utilized by the Baby Crissy dolls. The box back explains how it operates.

Beautiful Crissy and Country Fashion Crissy as they appeared in 1982. Modern collectors prefer that Ideal had used the original Crissy molds to resurrect the Crissy name. These reissue models did not enjoy the popularity of the early Crissy dolls.

Kerry

1971: Kerry, stock #1056-1, white only

A natural progression for any popular doll, especially a fashion doll, is to create friends and family for her. Crissy's new friend, Kerry, was introduced to the world in 1971. What a gorgeous girl she is! She has a slight smile and a dimple in her chin! With her fabulous green glassene eyes and divine champagne blonde hair, Kerry is absolutely stunning. Her short foundation hair is styled in a chin-length page boy cut with no layering. She is very fair skinned.

Kerry's outfit is a jazzy little short-sleeved, elephant print romper in two-tone green. Different versions of Kerry's romper are made from slightly varying fabrics; sometimes her outfit is made from a tightly knit synthetic fabric, and other times from a cotton blend with a different texture. At any rate, she always dons a matching green bow at her neckline and green shoes made in the usual early Crissy style.

Much like the 1971 Movin' Groovin' Crissy box, Kerry's box features an illustration of the doll with tons of curling blonde hair swirled around her face. Here again, we find the three small photographs of Kerry with her hair extended to different lengths, just like those on the Crissy doll's box.

The description from the Ideal catalog says it all: "Everything about this 17 1/2" (note: she is actually 18" tall) colleen says she's from the Emerald Isle. Kerry's beautiful green eyes (like a morn' in Spring), her finely sculptured face and graceful limbs will "steal your heart away." And her long flowing tresses can . . . grow from a short bob to knee-length. Of course, she fits all of Crissy's clothes."

Kerry's tentative smile gives her a thoughtful look.

Tressy

1970: Gorgeous Tressy, stock #1048-8

Toy history aficionados know that in the 1960s, the Ideal Toy Corporation acquired the American Character Company, along with all the old issue names and the copyrighted concepts. One of those American Character names acquired, "Tressy," was a smaller-sized fashion doll designed to compete with other popular fashion dolls of the 1960s. She had an extended wardrobe, and she was a grow-hair doll whose hair retracted by means of a key. It seems the name "Tressy," was resurrected by Ideal to be used for the Sears exclusive grow-hair doll.

"Gorgeous Tressy," as she was originally called, was initially offered in the 1970 Sears catalog. She wears an orange and white geometric print dress with matching panties trimmed in white lace. Her shoes are black, made in the style of Crissy's. In 1970, Gorgeous Tressy was issued only in a white version, but in 1971, this doll, dressed in this outfit, appeared in the Sears Wish Book as a black doll only. With this issue, the doll's name was shortened from "Gorgeous Tressy" to simply "Tressy." The white version of the doll was offered as Movin' Groovin' Tressy (although her box called her "Posin' Tressy").

Some Tressy dolls in 1970 came with a bonus hair care set. It was common for any of the grow-hair girls sold through Sears to be sold with a bonus item only available through this store. The number one Crissy sold through Sears, for example, had a special floor length gown in the same box.

In 1972, a glamorous bride gift set was offered in the Sears Toy Catalog. This set is quite rare.

The first Ideal Tressy to be issued and her box have a different look. She is particularly hard to find.

1971: Posin' Tressy, stock #1024-9

Tressy is a unique individual. Her coal black hair and vivid blue eyes give her character. She has a closed but smiling mouth, the lightest blue eye shadow, and high cheekbones. Like the other big girls after mid-1969, her 'tail only came to below her bottom.

Posin' Tressy is dressed in an aqua satin minidress with white lace sleeves and matching panties of aqua satin. She wears a matching sash decorated with a white enameled metal "buckle." Her shoes are aqua.

A nice feature is her swivel waist, just like Movin' Groovin' Crissy's waist. As mentioned, the 1971 Sears Wish Book actually called her "Movin' Groovin' Tressy," but, as one can see, this isn't what was on her box.

The box has beautiful graphics on it. Drawn rather than photographed, Tressy looks adorable.

Later, newer variations of Tressy appeared on store shelves but were not Sears exclusives. The 1983 Fashion Tressy doll looked very different from earlier Tressy dolls; she was made from different molds and had different hair. Though still a hair play doll, the new Fashion Tressy's hair didn't grow. Instead, she came with a "permanent wave" kit, a hair styling booklet, ribbons, and curlers. She was produced in blonde (stock #12716), brunette (stock #12732), auburn (stock #12740), and as a black doll (stock #12724).

Posin' Tressy is fairly hard to find. Her posin' body is actually the same body as the Movin' Groovin' Crissy body.

There are many variations in Tressy's Sears' Exclusive wedding gown. The lace varies as does her wrist corsage. Some sets have veils, and others have a long ribbon hair ornament with a flower attached.

Brandi

1972-1973: Brandi, stock #1068-6, white only

Crissy's new friend Brandi made her debut in 1972. A platinum blonde with sun-bronzed skin, Brandi is very much a glamour girl. She sports a darling orange heart-shaped tattoo on her right upper cheek just beneath her eye. Two tiny braids from her foundation hair extend to behind her ears, framing her face and giving her a carefree, cheerful look. Curiously, this doll does not have the usual glassene eyes that most of the grow-hair girls have, but painted blue eyes, instead. She was produced for two years.

Brandi wears a sweet orange swimsuit that laces at the chest. Her shoes are lace-up-the-leg orange clogs.

Her waist is a swivel waist that makes her poseable. Like all the big grow-hair girls, she was made from the same body and limb molds.

The box has a photograph of Brandi on the front posing in an outdoor scene. This is one darling doll!

Brandi's demure heart tattoo was somewhat of a bold move for Ideal. Not too many girls had tattoos at that time.

California tan Brandi borrowed Movin' Groovin' Crissy's body, but had style all her own.

24

Chapter 2

The Small Girls

The Ideal Toy Company didn't stop with just the bigger, 18-inch dolls in the grow-hair line. A beautiful collection of smaller dolls was produced, too. Production commenced with the first small girl, Velvet, who stood 15 inches tall. Shortly thereafter, Mia, Cricket, Dina, and then Tara followed, all the same height as Velvet. Even smaller was Cinnamon, who at first had no name of her own, but was called "Velvet's Little Sister." At 12 inches, Cinnamon was the smallest of the grow-hair collection.

Interestingly, just as Crissy and all of the big girls shared the same molds for the dolls' bodies, arms, and legs, Velvet and company did, too. Each of the small doll's heads, however, was painstakingly sculpted, making each of Crissy's younger companions a lovely, fresh-looking individual. Their varying skin tones and hair colors as well as little details—like a cute grin, sweet dimples, a darling expression, and incredible eye coloring—make them each unique, giving them each a personality all of her own.

Most collectors will find immediately that there is a bit of a family connection between the big girls and the small girls. Velvet was marketed from the beginning as Crissy's cousin. In fact, her box introduced her as "Crissy's cousin Velvet." Brandi and Dina, while not officially dubbed cousins, share characteristics that hint they are related: both are suntanned blondes, both have tattoos, both wear clogs, and both have painted, rather than glassene, eyes. Then, there are the Sears store exclusives, Tressy and Cricket. While it is true that Tressy and Cricket look very much different from one another, Tressy was sometimes available with a wedding gown packed in her box, and Cricket had a bridesmaid's gown. So, there was definitely some cross-marketing there. And we can't forget Velvet's Little Sister, as she was known that first production year. We came to know her as Cinnamon.

For each year of their production, Crissy's and Velvet's boxes resembled each other. The similarities usually were in the graphics and the design layout. The colors may have been different, but the design was obviously similar.

A colorful pair of small girls: (left) Velvet in "Kelly Coat" (1971) and (right) Dina wearing "Peasantries" (also known as "Loverly" 1971).

Velvet could never say she didn't have a thing to wear! There were 26 outfits—other than the clothes the dolls were issued in—available for the small girls. Here are few of them.

Velvet

Her striking violet-hued eyes and light blonde hair make it easy to spot Velvet in a crowd. Velvet made her debut in 1970. Most issues of the Velvet doll corresponded with issues of Crissy, and this was always the case from 1971 on with the release of Movin' Groovin' Crissy and Movin' Groovin' Velvet. Each Velvet issue was packed in her box with tube-like hair rollers bobby-pinned to the sides of her head in the sideburn area. When these were removed, her hair fell in neat ringlets. With the passage of time, though, these have usually straightened.

Each Velvet came in a uniquely designed box. The only exception was some store catalog Velvet dolls that came in a brown cardboard box. Generally, extra outfits were enclosed as a bonus. These outfits were "leftovers" from previous issues.

1970: Velvet, stock #1035-5 (white) and #1036-3 (black)

The first issue of the white Velvet doll wears a purple velvet-like dress, light pink or white panties, and purple shoes. The black Velvet of this debut year models the same dress in lavender with lavender shoes. Topping off the doll's 'tail is a matching velvet ribbon tied in a bow. Her box has a drawing of Velvet on the front, in the classic side view. The purple dress is also available in a waleless corduroy.

Above: A number one Velvet, in her original-issue velvet dress. This dress was sometimes issued in a waleless corduroy fabric. Finding a doll with her corkscrew curls is not an easy feat.

Box: Dolls sold in Canada were required to have both English and French on the boxes. The lithography wasn't as high quality as found on the American-issue boxes, but otherwise, they appear to be the same.

1971: Movin' Groovin' Velvet, stock #1027-2 (white) and #1091-8 (black)

This production year was a banner year for Velvet, as she came in two issues. Movin' Groovin' Velvet was the first one. She had a new swivel waist so that she could twist her torso and stand in graceful, relaxed poses.

Her basic outfit is a pink party minidress, matching panties, and purple shoes. The black doll is dressed identically.

The box has a drawing of Velvet's face from the front, and three oval photographs of her with varying hair lengths. The black doll has the same box, but her drawing shows her with dark skin, and her hair is colored in with purple even though she has black hair. The doll came with a hair styling booklet and a hair brush.

Movin' Groovin' Velvet with her new poseable waist is just as beautiful as ever in her new party dress in 1971.

1971-1973: Talky Velvet, stock #1028-0 (1971, white only) and stock #1095-9 (1972-1973, white only)

This Velvet spoke six phrases according to the Ideal catalogs of 1971-1973. She is a pullstring talker. The pull tab is in the shape of a butterfly and comes out of her lower back, under her grow-hair knob. Her outfit is a comfortable-looking, yellow quilted bathrobe with matching yellow shoes. Her hair care accessories in the package included large and medium hair rollers, a brush, ribbons, and bobby pins. She only came in a white version.

Her 1971 box is extremely similar to Movin' Groovin' Velvet's box, but the oval photographs show her wearing her bathrobe. The 1972-1973 versions come in a "photograph" box instead of a "drawing" box. On the front of these boxes is a photo of her in her robe. Actually, all the 1972 newly issued grow-hair girls came in photograph boxes.

Talky Velvet says:
"Come play with me."
"My hair grows."
"Hi, I'm Velvet."
"Comb my hair, please."
"I want to be your friend!"
"I want to wear my new dress!"

Velvet is comfortably dressed and ready for a slumber party (and can talk all night, too)!

1972: Look Around Velvet, stock #1093-4 (white) and #1098-3 (black)

In the early 1970s, the groovy grow-hair girls were always doing something new! The year 1972 proved to be no exception. The Look Around Velvet still had her trademark long, growing hair, but now she also had a pullstring on her back that, when pulled, enabled her to look back and forth and side to side. The pull tab is in the shape of a butterfly, just like Talky Velvet's. Both the white and the black doll wear a cute little plaid taffeta minidress, reminiscent of Look Around Crissy's long, plaid, holiday-styled gown, and panties made of the same taffeta fabric. A ribbon sash and a pink silk flower adorn her waist, giving her a festive appearance.

Quite noticeable about this doll is her long neck stem. The obvious disk in her upper neck area is part of her "look around" mechanism. While a bit unsightly, she is an interesting addition to a grow-hair collection.

1973: Velvet with a Beauty Braider, stock #1113-0 (white) and #1114-8 (black)

The year 1973 was a bit uneventful for little Velvet . . . there was only one issue for this year, the Velvet with a Beauty Braider. Threading sections of the doll's hair through the four slots of this new styling device enabled young hairdressers to weave Velvet's long tresses into elegant braids. Actually, the directions were a bit confusing and even big girls must have had trouble with it. But, once one got the "hang of it," it really did form very nice, thick plaits. This same tool appeared in the Crissy's Beauty Parlor set as well.

The white and the black doll are dressed identically in a darling light lavender print dress with a matching velvet sash, and panties of the same print. Her shoes are lavender, too. She also comes in a photograph box. Note that the box bears a striking resemblance to the corresponding Crissy issue of that year, Crissy with a Swirla-Curler.

The rich jewel tones of Look Around Velvet's dress go wonderfully with her purple eyes.

Above: The hair play theme was taken to the next level in 1973 with the addition of hair styling devices in the doll's box.

Box: Sometimes, the back of the box was different from the front, and just as interesting as the other side, too!

1974: Velvet with the New Swirly Daisies, stock #1211-2 (white) and 1215-3 (black)

Again, in 1974, there was only one new Velvet issued, the Swirly Daisies Velvet. To create exciting hairdos whether Velvet's hair was short or long, the young stylist could incorporate the new Swirly Daisies hairdo dangle into Velvet's hairstyle. This little gizmo, which resembles a string of daisies, is heavily wired so that it can be bent and twisted to form a veil of purple flowers or a lovely wreath.

Both the black and the white doll wear a little minidress in a plaid print, trimmed with a velvet sash. The doll's panties match her dress, and are constructed of the same material. She wears lavender shoes. This would be the last Velvet issued until she appeared in the 1981 Ideal buyer's catalog.

Ideal's Look Around Velvet, Illfelder Toy Company, NY, NY

This doll was issued in a very unusual way. The doll was boxed for the Illfelder Toy Company, but acknowledgment was given to Ideal on the box. The box is an open style with no lid, and it is covered with shrink-wrap. This Velvet did not come with any accessories. It is assumed that this doll was sold to be a sort of store special even though Look Around Velvet was available at most toy and department stores. No date was stamped on the box.

This Velvet issue is somewhat hard to locate, but it is well worth the effort to find her.

The Illfelder Toy Company's Look Around Velvet: notice how her corkscrew curls are rolled around tubes and held with hairpins. This is how all Velvet dolls, except the 1981 issue, were packed.

Mia

1981: Velvet, stock #8536-5 (white) and #8540-7 (black)

Velvet magically made a reappearance in this production year. While she didn't talk, look around, or come with a crown of purple swirly daisies, her hair still grew, but with a pullstring instead of the usual "belly button and knob" system. The quality of the vinyl that Ideal used changed a bit with this issue. Her skin tone is prettier, more peachy in color. Her short foundation hair is curlier and has a side part instead of the usual middle part that the earlier dolls have. The white and the black dolls are dressed identically in a white dress edged in lace with a pink ribbon around the waist. Although some versions of the dress have sleeves, most of the dresses are sleeveless. Some 1981 Velvets wear white wedgie-type Mary Jane shoes like Crissy's, but others appear in the usual white T-strap Velvet shoes. This was the last appearance of the Velvet doll.

Touted as a "striking new window package" in the Ideal catalog, her box is bright pink and magenta.

The final issue of the Velvet doll. This doll does not have the corkscrew curls on the sides as the others do. Her skin tone is more peach toned than previous issues'.

1971: Velvet's Beautiful Friend Mia, stock #1059-5 (white only)

After 1969 and 1970 had come and gone, it was clear to the Ideal toymakers that they had a good thing going. So the following year, Mia was introduced, and was quite well received. She seems to be somewhat difficult to find mint in the box, indicating that she was a very good seller.

With an impish grin that could melt even the coldest heart, Mia has a charm all of her own. As the first brunette to debut in the grow hair family, she is definitely unique. Her white teeth were individually molded, and her face is exquisitely detailed with dimples and laugh lines. Her wonderful blue eyes go very nicely with her little blue bubble romper. It has a white Peter Pan collar trimmed with lace and a tiny navy blue bow just below the collar. Her shoes are baby blue and are in the style of her friend Velvet's T-strap Mary Janes.

There is no doubt about it . . . Mia has character.

One can't help but smile when Mia is smiling back at you.

Posin' Cricket

1971: Posin' Cricket, stock #1026-4 (white only)

Posin' Cricket, a Sears store exclusive, is a darling doll. She seems to be a corresponding issue to the Sears Tressy doll. Typically, she sports big brown eyes, but a few Crickets were produced with blue eyes. Her hair is a wonderful copper color, and the sculptural work on this doll is marvelously detailed, from the pink apples in her cheeks to her friendly, open-mouthed smile. She wears a dark peach, plaid A-line dress with an orange velvet sash and matching panties. Her shoes are dark orange and somewhat shiny. A small barrette, made of the same orange velvet as her sash, and held in place with a plastic pick, adorns her hair. Her foundation hair parts on the right side.

A special edition of Cricket was released with a light aqua bridesmaid's gown packed inside her box (page 126).

Here is a gorgeous blue-eyed Cricket with her 'tail still wrapped. Her hair is more auburn, and her eyes are similar in color to Mia's eyes. (Blue-eyed Cricket courtesy of Frank Sposato.)

Hard-to-find Posin' Cricket complete with her barrette. The graphics on the box are fabulous.

Dina

1972-1973: Dina, stock #1037-1 (white only)

Dina was introduced as a counterpart to the larger Brandi doll and as a new friend for Velvet. The Ideal buyer's catalog calls Dina "a new tall 'n tan friend from the West Coast to play with." Truthfully, she is only 15 inches tall like her friend Velvet. But she is tan. Her big toothy grin and perky dimples make her adorable. She has a swivel waist and champagne blonde hair. The butterfly tattoo that she originally had on the outside of her right knee is oftentimes missing, even on mint-in-the-box examples. Like all of the new grow-hair girls (Dina, Brandi, and Velvet's Little Sister) introduced by Ideal in 1972, she has painted eyes instead of the usual glassene sleep eyes. She wears a short overall-type bathing suit in a lavender animal print and white lace-up clogs that are smaller than the clogs the big girls wore. She resides in a photograph box, like all of the 1972 issues.

Darling Dina is ready for a swim. Notice the butterfly tattoo on her right knee as depicted on the box. This is nearly always missing, even on mint-in-the-box examples.

Tara

The grow-hair Tara doll was introduced as not just an adaptation, but as an original; there was no white counterpart. She was the only "black only" issue by Ideal with so-called black features. With her black eyes, black hair, and pretty berry red lips, Tara is authentically beautiful. In keeping with the hair play theme, she also has soft, lustrous hair that grows. Her short, non-growing hair has no part in it, and the short braids at her temples are tied with white ribbons.

She wears a yellow gingham pantsuit and matching yellow shoes in the usual Velvet T-strap style. The knob on her back is molded in the same color as her skin tone, while very many of the other grow-hair girls in the black version have light skin tone knobs. She came in a photograph box. On the front of the box she is pictured by herself, and on the other side, she is shown being lovingly held by a little African-American girl. It was one of the prettier boxes produced.

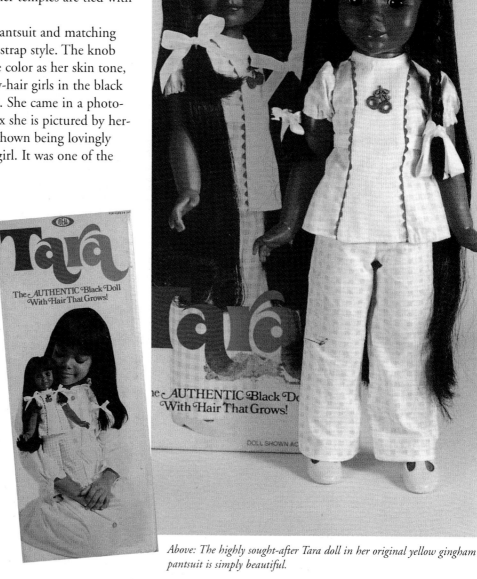

Above: The highly sought-after Tara doll in her original yellow gingham pantsuit is simply beautiful.

Box: The back of Tara's box is another example of how charming some of the boxes look.

Velvet's Little Sister

1972: Velvet's Little Sister, stock #1069-4
(white only)

The year 1972 held out a surprise to grow-hair girl fans! Now Velvet had a little sister in addition to cousin Crissy! Unfortunately, she would not be given a name of her own until the following production year. Instead, her box read: "You give her a name!"

She has big, blue painted eyes, copper-colored red hair, and two little well-molded white teeth showing at her top lip. Her stocky little body is only 12 inches tall. She has baby fat . . . that can be seen by the chubbiness of her knees. She wears a two-piece, bright orange polka-dot shorts set and uniquely styled orange T-strap shoes. The neckline and armholes of her outfit are trimmed in extra tiny eyelet lace, and there's a white ribbon sash around her middle.

She was presented to the buying public in a photograph box. Notice that the doll on the box has quite pronounced, over-sculpted knees. Fortunately, this didn't appear on the doll itself. The doll on the box must certainly be a prototype Little Sister.

Sometimes, one can find a non-played-with doll with the hair still wrapped in its original cellophane. This example, seen in the photograph, has this with the tissue curl wrap covering the hard curl at the end of her 'tail. What a darling!

Finding a grow-hair doll in this condition is a doll collector's dream-come-true!

Velvet's Little Sister, Cinnamon

1973: Cinnamon with a Hairdoodler, stock #1067-8 (white) and #1085-0 (black)

Finally, Ideal gave Velvet's Little Sister a name, Cinnamon. She was the same doll from the previous production year, with a twist. Packed in her box was a "Hairdoodler." This device consists of a cone that is hidden in the grow hole on the top of little Cinnamon's head, a barrette, and a butterfly at the end of a string. The young stylist attaches the barrette to the end of the doll's 'tail, pulls the string, and, *violà*, Cinnamon's long locks are transformed into an instant pile of curls. This device also was included in the 1973 issue of Crissy's Beauty Parlor.

Cinnamon wears an orange polka-dot outfit similar to the one she wore the previous year, but this time, instead of eyelet lace trim, her blouse has a large white, lace-trimmed collar decorated with a green bow. Her shoes are the same orange T-strap shoes as the 1972 doll's. She was sold in a photograph box that is very similar to most of the other 1973 grow-hair girl issues.

1974: Cinnamon with the New Curly Ribbons, stock #1212-0 (white) and #1216-1 (black)

Cute little Cinnamon got a new outfit in 1974, a denim short coverall over a yellow gingham blouse. It is actually constructed as a one-piece outfit. A cute flower-pot appliqué decorates the bib. As an added bonus, some Cinnamon dolls came with the 1973 outfit included in the box. Both outfits are pictured below, modeled by two dolls. Cinnamon herself didn't change; her face paint and modeling were the same as the previous two years.

Her long Curly-Ribbons hair-styling device has a cone that is inserted in the grow hole on top of her head. Then, her 'tail hair is intertwined into it for a new and interesting style. The "ribbons" are heavily wired and bendable, and the ends are tipped with flower shapes. Her box is a photograph box and is very similar in style and design to the Crissy with Twirly Beads and the Velvet with Swirly Daisies boxes.

Above: The box is very similar in design to the other 1973 issues, Swirla-Curler Crissy and Beauty Braider Velvet. Perhaps a tie-in was intended?

Box: Another great view of the back of a grow-hair doll box.

Black Cinnamon helps model the other outfit packed in the box with Curly Ribbons Cinnamon. The black doll wore navy blue shoes when sold in this outfit, however.

Chapter 3

Baby Crissy®

The Baby Crissy® doll is a significant member of the grow-hair family. Like the pre-teen Crissy doll, Baby Crissy has the ability to grow incredibly long, "stylable" hair—despite the fact that she is a young infant. The exception came in the mid-1980s when the name Baby Crissy was resurrected for another, completely different doll who lacked the grow-hair capability.

Baby Crissy is a large doll, created to be life-sized. She was supposed to represent a nine-month-old at 24 inches. Her target audience was younger children. In fact, the Ideal catalog shows her with younger girls. Commercials for the pre-teen Crissy doll featured girls in an older age category, from about ten to twelve.

The sculptural work for the Baby Crissy doll is nothing short of remarkable. Her sweet, open smile reveals a row of molded white teeth, and her exquisitely modeled feet and hands look like an actual baby's. She even has baby fat on her legs. She is reminiscent of the Ideal Playpal family of the early 1960s.

From year to year, from 1973 to 1982, Baby never changed in appearance. She always had auburn growing hair and black, non-sleep eyes. Each Baby Crissy also had what the Ideal catalog called "foam soft 'Magic Skin.'" This new "skin" was very different from the Magic Skin of the 1950s that deteriorates. Instead, it was a pliable vinyl with wonderful coloring.

Advertisements stated that Baby Crissy was able to wear layette-sized clothing, which accounts for why she often appears at doll shows and sales, antique shops, and flea markets in baby clothes. Unfortunately, without her original-issue clothes or box, it is impossible to tell in which year an early-issue Baby was made.

She always came home barefoot, as no footwear was ever included. No clothing was sold separately for her, but this didn't seem to matter, as she was one popular baby!

Baby Crissy as she appeared through the years, 1973 to 1995.

During each of Baby Crissy's first five production years, she was presented in a darling pink diaper set (top and bloomers). Minor variations, including different pockets and collars, appeared in the diaper set throughout all the years she was produced. The black Baby Crissy generally came in a lavender diaper set made with the same variations.

The box during these early production years shows four different photographs of Baby on all four sides.

Her 'tail is attached to a pullstring and a large plastic ring that activates her hair growing capabilities. When the ring is pulled, her hair retracts in; when the 'tail is pulled, her hair lengthens.

To date these early dolls, one would really need to rely on the clothing and the box in which the doll was purchased. As mentioned, the variations in the early-issue clothing were minor; usually the pocket and the collar varied somewhat. The box is the best way to tell what year a doll was made. For instance, recently on the World Wide Web, a white Baby Crissy was offered in a 1982 box; however, the doll was no doubt wearing an old, earlier factory stock outfit. She was also pictured in the auction advertisement wearing the lavender Baby outfit that came on early black dolls. It was doubtful that this doll outfit and box were put together by the dealer to earn a higher price, since the doll's head was wrapped in factory plastic, and the box was still sealed as well. Due to the oddity of this clothing combination, it realized a high price.

Two darling Baby Crissy dolls in their issue clothing.

Baby Crissy doll's box is as sweet as she is gorgeous. The white Baby Crissy box has a white child playing with Baby Crissy on it.

1981: Baby Crissy®, stock #1462-1 (white) and #1457-1 (black)

In 1981, Baby was reissued, again made from the same molds and with the same hair and eyes as the 1970's babies. This time, however, she wore very different clothing. She is nothing short of adorable in her white, sleeveless bubble romper trimmed in gingham. Like the 1970's Baby Crissy dolls, she was issued without shoes or booties.

Her box is pink with a darling photograph of her on the front. Hand-drawn graphics appear on the sides and back.

The box back helps to identify her as a nine-month-old. She certainly has a lot of hair for that age!

Looking summery and cool in her white romper, Baby Crissy sits next to one of the boxes in which she was issued.

39

1981-1982: Baby Crissy®, stock #8526-6 (white) and stock #8527-4 (black)

Again, Baby looks the same, wearing the same clothes as the previously mentioned issue, but now she can be found in two different boxes. One box is pink with red and purple stripes running along three sides of it. It has a large window on the front, so the doll can see her new owner. The other box is stock numbered the same, but it is pink, lavender, and aqua. The Baby dressed in the white romper will appear in either one of these boxes, but some versions of this issue Baby, dressed significantly differently in a pink gingham dress and bloomers, appear only in the pink, lavender, and aqua box. This particular issue is fairly hard to find.

This outfit is nearly impossible to find, but a precious one to have.

This box is particularly flimsy, being made of thin cardboard. Baby Crissy at least, can see out at her new owner through the window.

1984: Baby Crissy®, stock #10105 (white) and #10106 (black)

This Baby Crissy bears no resemblance to the Baby Crissy of previous years. Cast in new molds, she is only 18 inches tall, and has molded hair topped with a little swatch of synthetic hair rather than the long tresses of a grow-hair girl. In fact, this sleep-eyed Baby was not created to be a grow-hair doll, and she had little hair play value. Instead, she is a drink and wet doll. She wears a diaper set of light blue polka dots, and, like the earlier Baby Crissys, she is barefoot. Some of these dolls have no topknot hair.

1984: Baby Crissy®, stock #10109 (white) and #10110 (black)

This edition is also a drink and wet doll. She has sleep eyes and rooted blonde hair that does not grow. Her clothing is a large printed yellow gingham dress and matching bloomers. She was also issued barefoot.

1984: Baby Crissy®, stock #10111 (white) and #10112 (black)

Basically another version of the same doll as above, this Baby also has sleep eyes and molded hair with a little tousled topknot tied in a bow on the top of her head. Instead of the blue polka-dot diaper set, she wears a long, white christening gown and a bonnet trimmed with lace.

Baby Crissy in name only, these dolls were made during Ideal's "white doll" era. Many dolls cast by Ideal at this time were very pale in color.

1985: Baby Crissy®, stock #10109 (white) and #10110 (black)

Still 18 inches and barefoot, Baby Crissy again sports rooted hair, but with no grow-hair gimmick. Her dress is a cornflower blue print with matching bloomers. She is a drink and wet doll.

1985: Baby Crissy®, stock #10111 (white) and #10112 (black)

This 1985 issue of Baby Crissy is basically the same as the 1984 issue bearing the same stock number. She still has molded hair and a christening gown. The biggest difference between the 1984 and 1985 dolls is that the new Baby Crissy has no topknot on the top of her head.

1985: Baby Crissy®, stock #10105 (white) and #10106 (black)

Again, Ideal released the same doll as the 1984 issue but in a different dress. This doll wears a party dress trimmed with lace and ribbons, but she is still barefoot. There is no hair swatch on top of her head. Believe it or not, this was not the last time we hear the name "Baby Crissy."

Yet another Baby Crissy issue, but she was not met with significant sales success.

These dolls were cute, but they just weren't Baby Crissy.

More Baby Crissy Dolls

By 1991, Ideal was owned by a company known as View-Master Ideal Group, Inc. This was a subsidiary of Tyco Toys, Inc. This company decided to reissue some old ideas by recreating the "Ideal Nursery." This was the Classic Doll Collection which consisted of reissues of Baby Crissy, Betsy Wetsy, Tiny Tears, and Baby Bubbles. Each of these dolls came in a black version, too.

The 16-inch Baby Crissy in this collection is very reminiscent of the original doll, unlike the issues of the mid-1980s. Her body is soft instead of molded plastic. She has black sleep eyes and auburn grow-hair that functions by means of the classic pullstring. She is still smiling, showing her white molded teeth. Donning a totally revamped outfit that looks nothing like her first issue outfits, she is darling in a blue chambray jumper dress with a mock white print shirt. And she wears yellow shoes with pink socks! A first for Baby Crissy!

In 1995, the Baby Crissy doll's eyes changed to green! They really looked great with her auburn hair. A 1991 issue is sitting next to her and modeling one of the sold separately "Ideal Nursery" outfits designed to fit her. This was the only time extra outfits were sold for Baby Crissy.

Baby Crissy is reborn in 1991, and she finally gets shoes for the first time ever!

Also in 1991, the same company issued Teeny Baby Crissy®. At a mere 10 inches, she is adorable. Her body is soft, and she has chubby arms and legs. Her soft, pink romper is really her body and, thus, not removable. She is barefoot. She has auburn grow hair and blue glassene sleep eyes. Her white molded teeth show in her smile. She came with a brush and comb. Some of these dolls have blonde hair!

Baby Crissy was reissued one more time in 1995. The company was called Tyco Playtime, Inc. Now part of the "Playtime Nursery," five dolls appeared in the Classic Doll Collection, in white and black.

This time, Baby was called Beauty Parlor Baby Crissy®. She was again released as a grow-hair girl, and came with her own brush and comb. But surprise! She had green glassene sleep eyes! This was another first for any Baby Crissy.

She is 16 inches tall, and her coverall baby outfit has bunnies, bows, brushes, and hair dryers printed on it. Her vinyl cape protects her outfit from whatever a little stylist cares to dish out! She wears white booties on her feet. Once again, just like all Baby Crissy dolls with the grow-hair ability, her hair retracts by means of a pullstring. The last of the reissued Baby Crissy dolls really were darling babies.

The Beauty Parlor Baby Crissy of 1995, the final Baby Crissy edition (up until that point, anyway).

Some of the Teeny Baby Crissy dolls were sold with blonde hair. This little baby has wonderful blue eyes. Her molded teeth seem to protrude too prominently, but she is cute anyway.

Chapter 4

The Clothes

For the first five years of the Crissy® doll's production, from 1969 to 1973, Crissy was very well dressed. For each of these years, Crissy was presented with a new array of fashion choices, ranging from mod blouses and bell-bottoms to festive party dresses and elegant evening gowns. Then, in 1970, a second line of clothing was produced for Velvet, to coincide with her release.

Each outfit was a fashion statement, a reflection of the fabulous and free 1970's style. The collections included nightwear, daywear, school clothes, and fun time fashions. The grow-hair girls' clothing designers paid close attention to detail, often creating scarves, chokers, belts, and hats to accessorize the dolls' outfits. It was this care and sense of style that made Crissy and her friends the most groovily-dressed dolls of the decade.

The packaging for Crissy's clothing is very indicative of the year the outfits were produced. It would behoove the novice collector, or even the advanced collector, to familiarize him or herself with the color and styles of the packaging, so that he or she can quickly estimate the outfit's year of production. The earliest outfits came in small cardboard boxes illustrated with the same profile drawings of Crissy and Velvet that decorated the boxes for the dolls themselves. The boxes opened at the top and had yarn handles: orange ones for Crissy, and purple for Velvet. By 1971, the dolls' outfits were sewn to cards covered with cellophane. A clear plastic hanger was included with each ensemble, inserted at the top of the card. Only during the 1972 production year was a third kind of packaging produced: a box with a clear cellophane "window" that allowed the buyer to view the outfit.

With the exception of the very first outfits—those packaged in the "profile" cardboard boxes—shoes were not issued with outfits. They were sold separately in blister packs that contained several pairs of shoes.

Absolutely a picture of perfection, this Sears special edition marabou-trimmed dress was packed in number one Crissy doll boxes. The box will have a round sticker on it that reads, "Sears Exclusive Crissy Gown Included." (Doll and dress courtesy of Cyndie Steffen)

1969

The first six outfits that were issued for the original "hair-to-the-floor" Crissy were given names every bit as unique as the fashions themselves. "The Groovy Jumpsuit," "The Turned On Mini," "The Fun Fur Cape," "The Bold Blazer," "The Sleeper Bells," and "The City Pants Look" all made Crissy the most hip pre-teen of the mod era. As noted, each of these early outfits was issued in a small cardboard box with an orange yarn handle. Illustrated with the trademark profile drawing of Crissy, the boxes definitely resemble the box for the first-issue Crissy doll. Since only Crissy was available in 1969, clothes for the smaller dolls had not yet been released.

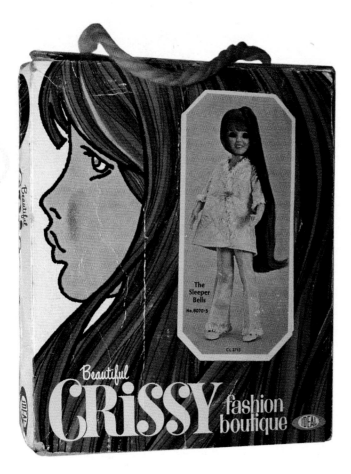

Finding one of these early boxes that has survived the ravages of time is a feat by itself. They are easily identified since they are so nearly identical to the number one Crissy box.

This hard-to-find outfit is called "The Turned On Mini" (1969). Her shoes are gold toned, but they sometimes come in black, too. Her fishnet hose are only thigh high. This is the only outfit that came with hosiery. She looks radiant!

Top: (left to right) "The City Pants Look," "The Turned on Mini," "The Fun Fur Cape." Bottom: (left to right) "The Groovy Jumpsuit" (known as "The Walking Jumpsuit" in the 1969 Ideal catalog), "The Sleeper Bells," and "The Bold Blazer" on a so-called brown-haired Crissy. ("The Bold Blazer" courtesy of Susan Mobley)

The first six outfits designed were sold exclusively for Crissy, as no other grow-hair girl had been produced, yet.

A number one Crissy models "The Fun Fur Cape" (1969). Black shoes were packed inside the box. The outfit was wrapped in orange tissue paper (just as the number one Crissy was in her box) and packed in the box. There is a rather large hole at the top of the hood for the Crissy doll's 'tail to go through. Some of the early issue outfits had pink hammer snap closures and some had the usual hand-sewn snaps.

1970

This year saw the release of three new outfits—"The Peace Poncho," "The Seventies Satin," and "The With It Knit"—and the reissuance of three outfits from 1969—"The Sleeper Bells," "The City Pants Look," and "The Turned On Mini." A line of clothing for Crissy's new cousin Velvet also hit the fashion doll runway this year, though the Ideal catalog did not give imaginative names to her outfits. Velvet's four ensembles, all in varying shades of lavender and purple, were called: "Lavender School Girl Jumper," "Baby Doll PJs," "Coat and Hat," and "Lace Pantsuit." Like Crissy's early outfits, Velvet's clothes came in cardboard boxes that resembled the doll's first-issue box. They were decorated with the same profile drawing of Velvet, and they even had purple yarn handles.

Two number one Velvet dolls wear darling early-issue outfits: (left) "Lace Pantsuit" and (right) "Coat and Hat," both 1970. Interestingly, all four of the first-issue outfits were made in shades of lavender and purple. This coat and hat are made of a soft (and warm) fleece-type fabric.

Called the "Here & Now Boutique," all of the first four Velvet outfits were wrapped in purple tissue and packed in a box such as this.

This catalog page featured stylized photos of Crissy modeling her new 1970 fashions. Some of the previous year's outfits were gone, but were replaced with three smashing new outfits. Crissy's 1970 collection included (left to right:) "The Sleeper Bells," "The Peace Poncho," "The City Pants Look," "The Seventies Satin," "The Turned On Mini" and "The With It Knit." These also were packaged in the cardboard box with the orange yarn handle. Very hard to find is "The Peace Poncho" ensemble.

When Kerry and Mia were introduced to the doll-buying market, their names were added to Crissy and Velvet's clothing packages. Each outfit in Crissy and Kerry's 1971 collection came sewn to an orange card covered with cellophane and was accompanied with its own plastic hanger. The card read, "Crissy fashions" across the top.

Crissy and Kerry sported eight new looks in 1971: "The Hob Nobber" ("Hob Nobbler" in the catalog, stock #8086-1), "Grape Drape" (stock #8085-3), "Surf's Up" (stock #8082-0), "The Drenched Trench" (stock #8083-8), "The Jean Machine" (stock #8087-9), "Gypsy" (stock #8084-6), "The Snuggler" (stock #8088-7), and "Funderwear" (stock #8081-2).

Some leftover stock from the 1970 Crissy clothing collection that originally came packaged in the "profile" cardboard boxes occasionally appears in the 1971-issue hanger packs. The outfits are hard to find packaged this way.

New outfits for Velvet and Mia were also packaged in the hanger packs, but they were sewn to purple cards. They were: "The Kelly Coat" (stock #8094-5), "Glad Plaid" (stock #8096-0), "Beachnik" (stock #8098-6), "Ruffled Up" (stock #8099-4), "Play Dots" (stock #8097-8), and "Smarty Pants" (stock #8095-2).

All ready for sweet dreams is Velvet in her "Baby Doll PJ" set.

In 1970, four precious outfits for Velvet were released. They are not easily located even for the avid grow-hair doll collector.

All of the 1971 outfits as shown in the Ideal catalog. Since Kerry and Mia were now made available in 1971, their names were included on the packaging, now a soft pack with a clear plastic hanger at the top. This was covered with cellophane. Top: (left to right) Crissy models "Hob Nobber," "Grape Drape," "Surf's Up," "Drenched Trench," "Jean Machine," "Gypsy," "Snuggler," and "Funderwear." Bottom: (left to right) Velvet wears "Kelly Coat," "Glad Plaid," "Beachnik," "Ruffled Up," "Play Dots," and "Smarty Pants."

The year 1972 was a banner year for Crissy and Velvet. Not only did three new friends, Brandi, Dina, and Velvet's Little Sister make their debut, but two new fashion collections were also introduced. Included in the Crissy and Velvet Dress Up Collection were four outfits for each sized doll. These were packaged in a box with a cellophane window. Crissy's read, "Designed for Crissy, Kerry and Brandi" at the bottom. Velvet's read, "Designed for Velvet, Mia, and Dina."

The big girls looked sophisticated in "Lemon Lite" (stock #8134-9), "Feminine Fancy" (stock #8135-6), "Blazering" (stock #8133-1), and "Very Vanilla" (stock #8132-3).

The small girls wore: "Checker Check" (stock #8144-8), "Ocean Motion" (stock #8143-0), "On The Lamb" (stock #8141-4), and "Blazering" (8142-2).

Fittingly, the second collection presented in 1972 was called the Crissy and Velvet Dress Down Collection. This collection was packaged in the familiar cellophane-covered

The Crissy and Velvet Dress Up Collection consisted of four exquisite outfits for each doll size. The Crissy doll's are exceptionally hard to come by but Velvet's appear quite frequently. It is noteworthy that Ideal took much time to style the hair of each doll modeling an outfit. Crissy looks glamorous, and Velvet is just as sweet as she can be!

Dina and Brandi were released in 1972, so their names were included on clothing packages along with Crissy's, Kerry's, Velvet's, and Mia's. The boxes for the Dress Up Collection are quite unique and so eye-catching.

hanger pack, but this time Crissy's outfits came sewn on lime green cards, and Velvet's on teal blue cards. The bottom of the larger dolls' cards read, "Designed Exclusively for Crissy, Kerry, & Brandi." The smaller dolls' cards read, "Designed for Velvet, Mia, & Dina."

New releases for the big girls were: "Patchworker" (stock #8119-0), "Hippie Happening" (stock #8115-8), "Lip Smackin' Good" (stock #8114-1), "Starshine" (stock #8112-5), "Moonshine" (stock #8113-3), "Funky Feathers" (stock #8117-4), "Burlap Bag" (stock #8116-6), and "An Overall Effect" (stock #8118-2).

The small girls were decked out in: "Super Stars" (stock #8121-6), "Cloud Movements" (stock #8126-5), "Kinky Kolors" (stock #8123-2), "Loverly" (this outfit is sometimes known as Peasantries-stock #8124-0), "Shortcuts" (stock #8127-3), "Dandy Denims" (stock #8125-7), "Frontier Gear" (stock #8122-4), and "Lemon Hang Up" (stock #8120-8).

A few variations in these outfits occurred during production. For instance, the "Dandy Denims" jeans for Velvet can appear either in very dark blue fabric or in a very light "bleach-spotted" blue. An even harder-to-find clothing variation is a rare version of Velvet's "Lemon Hang Up" vest. The vest is generally made of a coarsely woven fabric, but it can occasionally be found in printed corduroy.

When Velvet's Little Sister was first introduced in 1972, she had only one outfit available, the orange shorts set in which she was issued.

Collectors searching for Crissy and Velvet clothing today will notice that Velvet-sized clothing appears on the market quite frequently—many times mint-in-the-package—while Crissy wear tends to be harder to find. This seems to indicate that the Crissy doll and her clothing were more popular when they were produced and sold more readily.

Such sophisticated ladies! (left to right) Brandi models "Blazering," Crissy models "Lemon Lite," Tressy looks delicious in "Very Vanilla," and Look Around Crissy looks remarkably older in "Feminine Fancy." ("Blazering" courtesy of Carolyn Burt)

After "Dressing Up" so much, the girls needed to dress down some, too. So, the 1972 "Crissy and Velvet Dress Down Collection" was born! Eight new outfits for each doll size were available. All were the very personification of the 1970s.

1973

The Crissy and Velvet Sweet 'N Lovely Collection of 1973 was just that. Crissy really did look lovely in her new green dress called "The Dreamer," and perky Velvet was ready for a day of fun in a short and sweet sundress called "Smocked." The collection also included a few reissues from the previous year.

Crissy's outfit assortment consisted of: "Summer Social" (stock #8153-9), "Double Dip" (stock #8154-7), "Skimmer" (stock #8155-4) and "The Dreamer" (stock #8156-2). "Hippie Happening" (stock #8115-8) and

"Funky Feathers" (stock #8117-4) were favorites reissued from 1972.

Velvet's new outfits were: "Blouson Battle" (8160-4), "Strawberry Smock" (stock #8161-2), "Pulled Together" (stock #8162-0), and "Smocked" (stock #8163-8). Velvet's long, purple, folk-inspired dress called "Loverly" (or Peasantries-stock #8124-0) and "Dandy Denims" (stock #8125-7) were also reissued from the 1972 collection.

The 1973 and 1974 Cinnamon did not have extra outfits sold separately.

"Sweet and Lovely" is just the way to describe this collection from 1973. Clothing was styled for everything from formal social gatherings to casual wear. Some of the clothing is particularly hard to locate today. Top: (left to right) "Hippie Happening," "Funky Feathers," "Summer Social," "Double Dip," "Skimmer," "The Dreamer." Bottom: (left to right) "Peasantries" (about half of the packages produced called this outfit "Loverly"), "Dandy Denims," "Blouson Battle," "Strawberry Smock," "Pulled Together" (somewhat hard to find), "Smocked."

Shoes

The shoe collection is being discussed separately from the clothing line since shoes were sold apart from the outfits after 1970. As mentioned earlier, the very early cardboard box-packed outfits included shoes, but by 1971, when the outfits were issued in the hanger packs, the dolls' shoes and boots were sold separately in blister packs. Each pack included several pairs of perfectly matched right and left shoes. The bottom of each shoe was inscribed with an *L* or an *R* indicating left and right.

Crissy and Velvet both had several shoe styles. The shoes were molded in soft vinyl and came in colors as diverse and eye-catching as the doll's clothes. Most shoe styles came in white, light pink, rose pink, navy blue, royal blue, baby blue, aqua, shiny "hot" orange, matte orange, red, brown (for boots), apple green, forest green, light yellow, dark yellow, purple, lavender, and black.

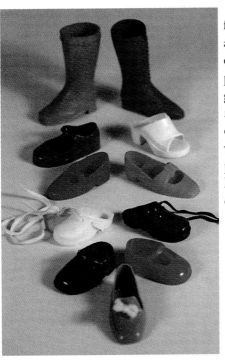

Crissy's fun and fashionable shoes are not only "far out"—they are practical, too. The grow-hair girls need shoes in order to stand up; without the support of a pair of heels, the dolls fall over backwards.

Grow-hair girl shoes: (clockwise from top left) a lavender boot styled for Velvet and friends with a squared-off toe; Crissy-sized brown boot with a rather pointed toe; Magic Hair Crissy's mules (these only came in white; there were green ones, but they were made for another Ideal doll); Crissy's bow flats in rose pink; Crissy's clogs in royal blue (bigger than Velvet-sized clogs); Cinnamon's original orange T-strap shoes; Shillman shoes made for Crissy (they don't fit any other doll) in blue (the buckle is missing so yarn is threaded through the two existing holes); navy blue T-strap shoes for black Curly Ribbons Cinnamon; yellow Velvet-sized clogs; Velvet-sized T-strap in red; and "new-style" Mary Jane wedgies in hunter green.

The Crissy doll's early shoes are the ones that are most easily recognized. They have a low heel, squared-off toes, and a "strap" decorated with a molded bow that crosses the top of the doll's foot.

Another style that actually came on later-issue boxed dolls, but which came packaged in blister packs, too, is the wedgie-style Mary Jane shoe. Like the classic Mary Janes, they have a single thin strap across the top of the foot, but instead of a small, distinct heel, they have a wedge for a heel.

Other styles include molded "lace-up" boots, and clogs with matching colored elastic ties that lace up to the knee. The boots have a rather pointed toe, molded laces, and a small heel. Orange boots were issued on the Movin' Groovin' Crissy, the only boxed issue wearing boots. Crissy's clogs are darling, too. The elastic laces are laced over the top of the clog and tied at the knee.

The smaller dolls have cute, but smaller shoes with a molded T-strap across the top of the foot. They also have a small heel to help them stand up. The collector needs to bear in mind that there are two sizes of clogs. The larger

Crissy (and Velvet) shoes were sold in blister packs in a variety of styles. Shillman shoes were made for the Crissy doll. They sport little metal buckles that come loose rather easily.

ones obviously are to be worn by the big girls, and the smaller size is for Velvet and company. Both sizes lace up the same way. Boots for Velvet have a square toe and have a "zipper" molded on the inside leg of each right and left boot.

Cinnamon, or Velvet's Little Sister, only came with one style shoe: T-strap Mary Janes with a very low heel. Her shoes always matched her outfits. They came in orange to compliment her first-issue ensemble, the orange polka-dot shorts set, or in navy blue to go with her short coverall outfit (on the black doll). She never wore clogs or boots.

It is important to note that none of the original Ideal Baby Crissy issues were released with shoes or booties.

Crissy's hanger pack clothes. The earlier one is the orange pack outfit.

Velvet outfits as they appeared in the cellophane-covered hanger packs. The purple pack was produced earlier.

Chapter 5

Cases and Luggage

Most serious doll collectors appreciate the value of adding cases and other luggage to their doll collections. A grow-hair doll collector is no exception. The Crissy® doll and her family had so many different kinds of cases, there is no doubt that having one or all of them adds significant interest to a collection. Besides, they can be quite handy for storing extra shoes and clothing items.

Some cases will be quite common and readily available. However, some of them may evade the collector for what seems like an eternity. For instance, any case made as a Sears store exclusive will be somewhat harder to find. Ideal Crissy cases were sold in most toy or department stores, whereas the exclusives were not. Therefore, they were not produced as plentifully.

All of the cases were elaborately lithographed with vibrant colors. The illustrations were "classic Crissy," always depicting the doll dressed in her finest clothes. Even the luggage collection made for a little girl's use was equally as beautiful. All are wonderful additions to any Crissy doll collection.

The Cases

1971: A Tote for Beautiful Crissy® and her Fashions

This case is copyrighted 1970, but it wasn't offered to stores through the Ideal catalogs until 1971. At 19 inches tall, this first-issue case has a handsome illustrated view of Crissy's profile. She is also illustrated wearing some of her famous first-issue outfits. This case unrolls to open up to two compartments, one large enough for Crissy to stand in, but the other rather small. It can only hold a couple of outfits at the most. The inside is yellow quilted vinyl.

1971: Crissy® and Friend Fashion Tote

Copyright marked 1970 on the inside of one of the compartments, this case looks very similar to the previously mentioned case, but appears to be a deluxe edition. It opens from the front and the back, has the very recognizable profile of Crissy only reversed, and has a red carry strap. Among the very mod swirls and paisleys lithographed on it are drawings of Crissy in some unrecognizable outfits. One side has accommodations for clothing on hangers. It is 20 inches tall.

This is the very first case ever issued for Crissy and her fashions. It is relatively easy to find for today's collectors.

This is the inside of one compartment of the 1971 issued Crissy and Friend Fashion Tote. It looks very much like a boutique, or maybe the inside of Crissy doll's closet?

1971-1973: Crissy® and Velvet Hair Fashion Tote

This case was an absolute MUST for Crissy and her cousin Velvet. It contained just about everything needed to coif Crissy's hair, including a small "hair dryer" that operated on one AA battery, a comb, a brush, four rollers, a ponytail holder, a hair bow, eight bobby pins, four clippies, two barrettes, and two yarn hair ties.

The illustrations show Crissy combing Velvet's hair. Mod flowers are printed on the top and sides. There is a red strap handle on top. The copyright date is 1970, but the case wasn't made available to buyers until 1971.

What an awesome set for the little hair stylist! What more could he or she possibly need to beautify a grow-hair girl?!

Above Left: This side has the swing-out arm to hold the hangers of all those terrific Crissy outfits that one is bound to acquire. The graphics replicate a dressing room.

Left: This deluxe case has the easily recognizable profile of the Crissy doll. The outfits illustrated on the side are unknown.

1972: A Tote for Beautiful Crissy® and Velvet Fashions

This case is copyrighted 1971, but, like the 1970 copyrighted cases released in 1971, it was released a year later, in 1972. This year, Velvet's name was added to the case, so that it now read, "a tote for Beautiful Crissy Velvet Fashions." In its design, the case is very much like the 1971 tote that only mentioned Crissy's name. In fact, other than the addition of Velvet's name, the graphics are identical. The interior is also the same, as is the handle.

As with many toys made throughout history, variations sometimes appear in Crissy's fashion cases. For instance, a 1971 case surfaced from Canada, which is marked the same way as the 1972 case, and has the same lithography, but is constructed differently. One side of the case is riveted together, whereas the typical 1972 cases are not. Also, the interior is smooth, not quilted. One of the most easily recognizable differences between the cases is the handle: the handle of the more unusual variation is white instead of red, and it is riveted in, not held in by a plastic disk. Both versions are 19 inches tall.

Looking familiar is this 1972 case that included Velvet's name with its second issue. One of the outfits pictured on the front is "The City Pants Look" from 1969.

Visible on this case that came from Canada are the rivets on the side and the white, riveted-in carry strap. Unique features such as this make doll collecting interesting, enjoyable, and fun!

1973: Crissy® and Velvet Fashion Tote

Pictured on the front of this pink case is the Look Around Crissy doll. It is a six-sided case with a carry handle that opens from the front and the back. Like most of the vinyl cases produced for this collection, it was shrink-wrap packaged and had a tag hanging from the handle.

This six-sided case is quite difficult to find, but a treasure when it is located. It opens on the front and the back.

The Luggage

1971: Miss Tressy Look-alikes

This set of luggage was a Sears store exclusive. The set consists of a shoulder bag (with very mod fringe), a hat box, a vanity case, and a train case. This set is quite hard to find. Another obscure piece is the brunette wig that replicates Tressy's hairstyle. At the top is an 18-inch hair switch that resembled Tressy's 'tail.

To locate this whole set for one's collection would be a major find!

The hard-to-find Miss Tressy Vanity Case is a Sears exclusive.

1972: Miss Crissy® and Miss Velvet Fashion Luggage Line

Fairly hard to find is the Miss Crissy and Miss Velvet luggage set. This set of matched luggage was designed mainly for the young doll owner, but the Ideal catalog says that it could be used by "Crissy and her 'mommy.'" It goes on to say that the pieces are "artfully decorated with the 'Miss Crissy' Look." They are that, indeed. The Miss Crissy luggage line is white with colorful, ultra-mod graphics, and the Miss Velvet luggage is baby blue with similar graphics. These cases were copyrighted in 1971.

Isn't the model for this picture cute?

Made with a little girl's personal use in mind, these cases do not turn up frequently today for the collector. They were rather roomy and well made, so they are usually in fairly good condition when found.

Steamer Trunks

1972: Crissy® and Velvet Fashion Steamer Trunk

This fashionable trunk, at 16 inches tall, is large and roomy, no doubt for the growing collection of Crissy clothes being released every year. Inside, there is a hanger bar, an accessory shelf, and a roomy storage bin.

World travel stickers are printed on the front as are illustrations of Crissy and Velvet looking particularly happy. The interior is baby blue vinyl. This trunk was copyrighted in 1971.

The travel stickers on this trunk were printed on, so they never came off. The girls have seen quite a bit of the world, as evidenced by the stickers they've accumulated!

The inside of this case is a beautiful shade of baby blue. It holds an ample amount of Crissy couture.

1971: Tressy and Cricket Fashion Steamer Trunk

Very similar to the Crissy and Velvet Fashion Steamer Trunk, this trunk is also large and roomy. Tressy and Cricket's faces are printed on the front. Stickers were included with the trunk to replicate travel stickers accumulated as the "girls" traveled. The interior is pink rather than baby blue vinyl. Other than that, this trunk is the same on the inside as the previously mentioned Crissy and Velvet Fashion Steamer Trunk.

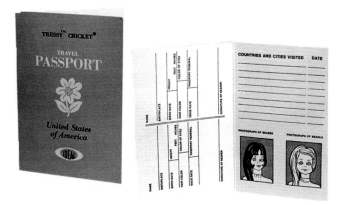

This unique item, the Tressy Cricket Travel Passport, came with the Tressy and Cricket Fashion Steamer Trunk. Since it is made of paper, it is oftentimes missing.

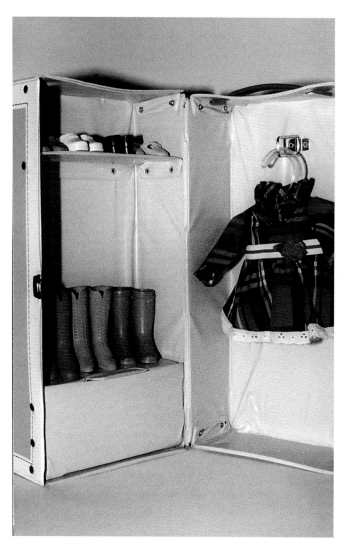

The interior of this steamer trunk is pink, but other than that it looks the same inside as Crissy and Velvet's steamer trunk.

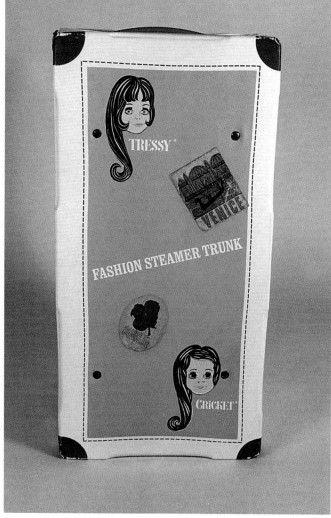

The stickers for this steamer trunk are actually stickers—not stamped markings. It appears that Tressy and Cricket were well-traveled, too!

Chapter 6

Furnishings

Several fashion dolls of the 1960s and 1970s not only had an ample wardrobe of clothing, but many also had nice furniture to augment their play value. The Crissy® doll's furniture was centered around both her fabulous mod wardrobe and the hair play theme that followed Crissy and friends throughout the years of their production.

1971-1972: Crissy® Clothes Rack and Closet Set, stock #8051-5

The Crissy doll's wardrobe may have been a whirlwind of stylish choices for the first two years of her production, but now at least she had an ordered place to store all her mod threads. The clothes rack consisted of a plastic frame with a hanger pole across the top and slanted shelves across the bottom for holding shoes. Two vinyl garment bags with clear sides—one larger than the other—were included to "protect" Crissy's clothing. Also included were four hangers, two each of orange and hot pink, all marked "Ideal." The box states that this set was for use with Crissy, Velvet, Mia, and Kerry.

To protect and store the doll's clothing, Crissy's little fashion advisor first hung an outfit on one of the set's bright hangers, and then placed it inside the garment bag on a notched hanger bar. Once she fit the hanger through the hole at the top of the garment bag, the bag was ready to be hung on the clothes rack.

This closet set was attractive, but limited in size. With all the clothing Crissy had, a young wardrobe consultant would need at least two sets to hold all those clothes!

This very minimal clothing rack holds very few clothes, but it is an imperative item to have in a grow-hair collection.

To achieve Crissy doll's crowning glory, no doubt the beauty parlor set would really come in handy. This set replicated a real salon with a chair and a styling console. The unique chair was designed so Crissy's grow-hair knob could slide into a slot, holding her steady so that she could sit firmly while all that brushing and combing was going on! In the console were two large drawers to hold most of the styling accessories. The brush and a few other items were too big to go inside.

Included in this wonderful set was: a styling chair, a Swirla-Curler, a Beauty Braider, a Hairdoodler, a special brush and comb, a styling booklet, and an assortment of ribbons, flowers, hair pins, rubber bands, and barrettes. Note that the Swirla-Curler, Beauty Braider, and Hairdoodler were accessories sold with certain grow-hair doll issues.

This set was designed to be used with all the grow-hair girls. Even Cinnamon, whose unique, flatter knob didn't allow her to be fit into the "slot," could sit in the chair—as a "seat belt" was included for her use!

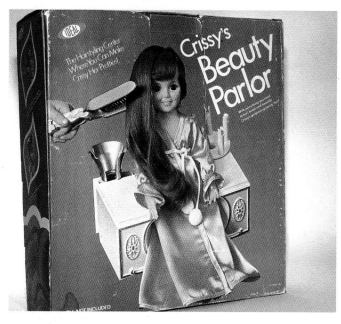

The back of the box shows Crissy getting her hair styled.

A wonderful set for the little hair stylist is this beauty parlor. There are so many items included that the grow-hair girl could have a new style every day of the week!

Chapter 7

Paper Goods

The advanced doll collector, after acquiring all of the doll issues in a collection, the clothing items, cases, and furnishings, usually goes on to obtain paper dolls, coloring books, games, and sewing patterns. Offering licensing agreements to other companies to make related items results in continued advertisement for a doll line and keeps interest alive. The Western Publishing Company of Racine, Wisconsin, was one company that took advantage of a licensing agreement as did the Simplicity Pattern Company.

The paper dolls that resulted from the efforts of Whitman were truly beautiful sets. They did a good job with the likenesses of the Crissy® doll and Velvet, but they took considerable license with the clothes. Some outfits were based on the original Ideal outfits; many were totally new ideas.

Some paper items do not survive well, so getting them can sometimes be a challenge. Oftentimes, they have many pieces, like paper dolls, games, and patterns. Also, these items were designed to be played with and were, for the most part, disposable. Even so, they can only increase the value of a collection, so they are worthwhile pursuits.

As a result of all this cross-marketing, there is a world of paper collectibles out there that just make doll collecting "plain ol'" fun!

Part of the fun of collecting paper items is finding the patterns for your favorite doll. These dolls are dressed in outfits from Simplicity pattern #6061, in both sizes. How "fitting!"

Patterns

The fine art of home sewing seems to have faded these days, but during the early 1970s, it was alive and well. If we ever forget what we wore during one era or another, we only have to find doll patterns from that generation to recall the fashions of the past. Each of Crissy's patterns is a study in mod era fashion. Palazzo pants, smock dresses, big bell-bottoms, ponchos, and halters all appear in the Simplicity patterns. Most of the Crissy patterns show drawings of dolls that very much resemble Crissy and Velvet, and their names are listed on the back.

There are other benefits to owning patterns for the grow-hair girls. Many times, there are more dolls to be found than original issue clothes. Using vintage fabrics with these patterns, the collector can create new clothes with a very authentic 1970s look. Try dressing nude dolls with newly constructed clothing and original shoes, making them the most unique items in the collection.

Simplicity Pattern Co., Inc.

Copyrighted 1969, Simplicity pattern #8519 was made in only one size for Beautiful Crissy. It featured a smock dress, a fringed dress, a bikini top, slacks, a minidress, vest, blouse, and a pantsuit.

Curiously, the doll pictured on the front has hair that grows to her feet, just like the 1969-issue Crissy doll. However, she is pictured as a blonde. It is more than obvious that this is a grow-hair doll, though, evidenced by the doll's short foundation hair.

1969: Simplicity #8519, one size

Printed in 1970, Simplicity pattern #9138 offered a long dress, a minidress, blouse, long skirt, vest, baby-doll PJs, a tunic, slacks, and a poncho. This pattern came in two sizes, 17-1/2-inch for the Crissy doll and 15-1/2-inch for Velvet. The dolls are illustrated as blondes, again with shorter foundation hair. This appears to have been a popular pattern. Many times, these outfits have appeared in box lot purchases of Crissy and family dolls and clothes. Some are extremely well made, demonstrating the talents of many mothers in the early 1970s.

Simplicity pattern #9698, 1971, also came in two sizes to accommodate the two different-sized dolls in the grow-hair collection. The outfits in this pattern were particularly charming: a long granny-style dress, a long jumpsuit, a Red Riding Hood style cape, a bridal gown complete with veil, a jazzy pair of shorts paired with a blouse and top, and a pair of knickers.

The wedding gown from this pattern is even prettier than the one issued by Ideal for Tressy since it has more detailed shaping. The Juliet sleeves and high waist are positively gorgeous. With the right hairstyle, a grow-hair girl looks great with this veil pattern.

1970: Simplicity #9138, two sizes for both sized dolls.

1971: Simplicity #9698, two sizes for both sized dolls.

In 1972, Simplicity pattern #5276 offered the following outfits: a jaunty blazer and slacks, a sailor suit, long "wrap" style culottes, a minidress, a tennis dress and shorts, and a long halter-style dress. This pattern was also available in the two different sizes, 15-1/2 and 17-1/2 inches.

The Crissy doll looks special in her two nautical-looking outfits included on this pattern. The blazer is quite reminiscent of a Navy uniform. And there isn't a doll around that wouldn't look great in that sailor suit!

Finally, in 1973, Simplicity pattern #6061 was printed in two sizes, too. A summertime bridal gown, a long dress, slacks, smock top, pantsuit, shorts set, and a lounging set were included.

The outfits on this pattern were pretty basic. They really lacked the detailing that the first Simplicity patterns offered. Still, Crissy and her friends and family look great in anything!

1972: Simplicity #5276, two sizes for both sized dolls.

1973: Simplicity #6061, two sizes for both sized dolls.

The McCall's Pattern Company

Though not showing the Crissy doll's face on the front, McCall's pattern #2182, copyrighted 1969, lists Crissy as one of the dolls it fits. Velvet was not listed. She had not been released yet. The outfits that could be made were two dresses, a pantsuit, a lined coat, a nightgown, and a robe.

The clothing resulting from this pattern is loosely constructed and rather simple in design. To make the clothes look good on a doll as striking as Crissy, one would need to use an extraordinarily unique fabric.

The outfits appear to be rather juvenile. Crissy, even though she is obviously a pre-teen, has a sophisticated look about her. It is a good thing that Simplicity created a line of patterns especially for her, as the McCall's pattern didn't really measure up.

1969: McCall's #2182, one size.

In 1971 and 1972, several patterns were made by Virginia Lakin for those who could knit and crochet. These patterns add interest to a grow-hair doll collection. Three patterns are pictured here.

Paper Dolls

Whitman, a division of the Western Publishing Company, produced the authorized editions of Crissy paper dolls. The sets were rather unique, and some "did" things. Imagine paper wigs! The following paper dolls are just some examples of the assortment available.

1970: Crissy®, Fashion and Hairstyle Boutique

Six pages of outfits and six paper wigs give this wonderful set charm. It is very colorful, and the doll itself has very short hair—perfect for adding the new styles of the paper wigs. The artwork on the back is beautiful.

Six paper wigs for Crissy added to the play value of this set. The clothes were made of heavy paper and were very fashionable, though not based on any of the Ideal outfits. The clothing was somewhat juvenile.

The back cover illustration is astoundingly beautiful!

1971: Crissy® and Velvet Paper Dolls

Most unusual is this paper doll set—featuring a black Velvet and a white Crissy. The collector will recall that the vinyl dolls were marketed as cousins. Certainly the Whitman company was to be congratulated for their forward-mindedness by including both races in one paper doll set. This oddity makes these paper dolls quite desirable. There were six pages of clothing for both dolls, and there was even a sleeping bag!

The paper dolls themselves are on the first page of the folder, and can be seen peeking through cut-outs in the front cover. There is a very interesting "Change-A-Hairdo Wheel" in the back meant to be attached behind the front cover. When the wheel is turned, the illustrations of Velvet and Crissy on the front cover change!

The most unique paper dolls in the collection: two cousins, two races.

These are the paper dolls on the inside, behind the front cover.

1971: Beautiful Crissy® Magic Paper Doll

This boxed Whitman paper doll set came complete with safety scissors and had all new outfits, none of which resembled Ideal's outfits. To keep the costumes on the paper doll, the doll had to be rubbed briskly to create static. The Crissy doll wore an orange top and panties set, and was supported by a small plastic ring stand.

Some of the outfits were cute; others were somewhat bizarre. The tennis outfit might be found in any pre-teen's closet, but a few of the outfits were created from an unusual combination of clothing items. For instance, one eccentric ensemble consists of a long-sleeved blouse and pair of shorts covered up by a knee-length dress. The dress is buttoned down only to the waist, leaving Crissy's knees showing. The outfit is completed with lace-up-to-the-knee sandals. The paisley-printed, knee-high boots included with another costume are also rather eye-catching. One thing was for sure with this set—it was colorful!

1972: Crissy® Magic Paper Doll

Also by Whitman, the Crissy Magic Paper Doll set was sold in a box instead of a folder. Included was a small plastic ring-shaped stand and plenty of clothes. The directions stated that in order for the clothes to stay on by means of static, the doll and the little fashion advisor's hands must be kept dry and dust free. Rubbing a clean dry cloth briskly over the doll kept the costumes in place. Whether or not that actually worked is questionable, but it is a neat concept.

A few of the outfits included in this set are the same as clothing issued by Ideal. There are plenty of outfits, too, that were originals made for the paper doll. Note the imagination involved in creating these outfits. They are so intriguing! The rain gear with the umbrella (somewhat bizarre-looking), the Hawaiian print fanny wrap and leg bracelet, the open-toed, lace-up boots, the ballerina tutu, and even the lavender, watermelon print, long dress give us a unique perspective on the fashions of the 1970s (maybe even the styles we don't remember)!

Eye-catching outfits in vivid colors make this an attractive paper doll set.

This set has the most unique and imaginative clothes in the grow-hair collection. Each outfit is distinctive.

Copyrighted MCMLXXIII, this Crissy paper doll set came in a folder. It came with six pages of clothes. This set really didn't "do" anything unique like the other sets, but it was equally as charming. A very large drawing of Crissy from the waist up graces the front cover, and the paper doll is on the back cover. She wears two cute pigtails and a buckled one-piece bathing suit.

The paper doll is found on the back of the cover.

These paper dolls make an attractive but "calm" paper doll set, compared to other ones made by Whitman.

Other Paper Products

1970: Velvet & Crissy® Shopping Spree Game

Velvet receives top billing with this set! Created by Whitman, this fun game, for two to four players, has tons of money and lots of things to shop for: a watch, a camera, a "pop album," a Teddy bear, shoes, clothes, sunglasses—everything for a young girl living in the mod era! The players earned money with good report cards, baby-sitting, odd jobs, birthdays, and weekly allowances.

The playing pieces are small Crissy dolls cast one each in yellow, blue, green, and red. By spinning the spinner, the player advances around the board accumulating money and purchases. The game is over when all the merchandise cards are taken up by the players. They then total up the value of the merchandise and the money. The winner is the player with the most of both.

The infamous profile drawings of Crissy and Velvet, the same ones that appear on the number one Crissy box and the first Velvet box, grace the front of this box. The drawings of the dolls on the playing board are attention-getters, though. The dolls appear quite older than the pre-teen-age girls we know them to be. Velvet looks to be about the age of her older cousin, Crissy.

A rather hard-to-find item, the Velvet & Crissy Shopping Spree Game taught the value of the allowance dollar!

This terrific set came with three stand-up paper figures, and each one had a different hair style. The vinyl clothing is pressure sensitive.

The real dolls pictured on the front of this play set are wearing early-issue clothing. The cape and the pantsuit appear to have been replicated in vinyl for this set, but the rest of the clothing items bear no resemblance to her real Ideal-wear.

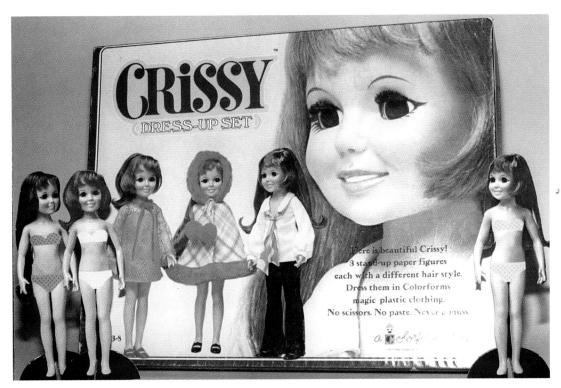

Above: Even the little ones could enjoy playing with Crissy! The three different dolls are pictured with the different hair lengths.

Left: Some of the outfits were easily recognizable (identifiable as they possibly could be when rendered in vinyl, at least).

Once again, Crissy is white and Velvet appears as black, even though they are cousins. The book does not mention that they are cousins, however. In fact, the girls look quite similar to the paper doll set of the same year. As one leafs through the book, one notices immediately that Velvet's family is illustrated as African-American.

The book has several activities: word scrambles, paper wigs, and a stuffable paper "rag" doll, among other things. The drawings show the girls with short foundation hair and long 'tails. We also learn a bit of trivia about Crissy: her pet is a poodle!

The story line has Crissy watching from her window as Velvet and her family move into a vacant house. The neighborhood girls form a club that gets involved in charitable activities. The story wraps up with Crissy, Velvet, and friends (which, by the way, do not have names like Kerry and Mia) hosting a party for orphans and giving them gifts of refurbished toys and dolls that were donated by the neighborhood . . . charming!

The charming story portrayed in this coloring book is worth the search to find it.

Chapter 8

Other Groovy Things

One would think that after discussing a vast collection of dolls, clothing, cases, and paper items, there wouldn't be much left. Still, to the contrary, there are other things that add much interest to a complete Crissy doll® and friends collection.

Naturally, since Crissy was a grow-hair doll with emphasis placed on hair styling play, there were other items sold to assist the young stylist in the quest for the perfect hairstyle. Of course, all these things were very "groovy."

1971-1973: Crissy Hair Dryer, stock #8064-8

How about a blast from the past? Remember when Mom used to walk around the house with a soft vinyl, inflated hair dryer on her head over her hair rollers? She must have had a long power cord! The Crissy doll's hair dryer was very similar, but it was battery operated. It really blew air to inflate the vinyl cap, which had funky flowers printed all over it. Of course, its case (decorated with a mod butterfly) had a carry strap, enabling Crissy or any of her friends to strap it to her shoulder and stroll around, too. Nostalgic yet?

Gorgeous Kerry is using the hair dryer, and modeling "Funderwear" (1971).

This awesome set is quite difficult to find. It came with a base that supported the makeup mirror, which is made of paper and foil. The base has depressions in it for the comb and brush, a can of simulated hair spray filled with perfumed water, the battery-operated curler warmer, the curlers, and the styling booklet.

Since this was manufactured for three production years, one wonders what happened to all of them. Sometimes, bits and pieces of the set appear in cases full of clothes and other Crissy items. Yet, as a complete set, it rarely appears. It is assumed that it was a popular set. It was almost a must for any little girl if she were to style her doll's hair. Therefore, this could account for the set's scarcity. This set also had dramatic counter appeal: it was neatly and attractively packaged. Surely, it must have been a big seller.

The small 3-by-3-inch booklet accompanying the set gives the doll owner numerous tips for changing the length and style of Crissy's hair. For example, to curl Crissy's auburn tresses, the book instructs young stylists to dampen the doll's hair slightly before setting, to use smaller rollers for the best set, and to leave the doll's hair to dry in the curlers overnight. Leaving the new curls unbrushed, the booklet explains, will create spiral curls. Other style suggestions included a ponytail with a party curl, a "crispy looking long braid," a "frothy flip," "criss-cross curls," "jaunty side ponytails," "side loveliness in a swirl," a "cascade of curls," and "curls and swirls," a style idea consisting of beautiful Grecian curls. Some of these hair styles appeared illustrated in this book.

This set is the extremely hard-to-find Crissy Hair Styling Set. The "hot roller" set turns up fairly frequently, but to find it in the complete styling set is nearly unheard of.

Here are the "hot rollers" from the set. It has "Crissy" in raised letters on the front and "Velvet" on the back.

Probably one of the most interesting items in the Crissy line, the Way-out Wig offered unique styling options when Crissy couldn't do a thing with her hair!

Oddly enough, the wigs are quite ill-fitting on Crissy. Using ample bobby pins helps keep them secure. The hair of the wigs is rooted into pliable clear vinyl bases. They came in two colors, blonde and brunette. There were also two styles: one was a layered look and the other was an "Afro-style," as it is called in the Ideal catalog.

The wigs came packaged in an attractive box on a Styrofoam head-form so the wig would keep its shape. Also included in the box was a rat-tail hairbrush. Crissy certainly looks distinctive with hair in colors rather than her own natural auburn. The wigs can be quite useful, too, if a Crissy doll is having a bad hair day!

The somewhat bizarre-looking Crissy's Way-out Wig is a bit hard to find.

Two Crissy dolls modeling their Way-out Wigs. Note: they are wearing clothing made by other manufacturers, not by Ideal.

This marvelous item has a copyright date of 1972. The fresh-faced little girl with freckles is simply charming with her Crissy modeling "Hippie Happening." This poster came with the Look Around Crissy doll, though it was not included in all Look Around Crissy boxes. This is a very desirable item to Crissy and family doll collectors. The story on the reverse side is captivatingly cute:

"This was the day Crissy woke up very mad, very sad, and very upset. Her hair flew every which way. Flip. Flop. Plop. And she got up, and sat by the window and thought; "It's no good to feel upset. I must tell HER how I feel." And her friends, Dina and Brandi and Velvet (and Velvet's little sister) came to see her. And they said, "Crissy, why do you look so sad?" "I love you all very much, Crissy said, "but what bothers me is a secret thing that I can tell only to HER."

"If you're going to tell a secret thing just to HER, you must look just right!" they cried. "We'll help you get ready." And they did.

"A dress! A dress! You need the right dress!," they cried, and clapped their hands, and ran over to the rack with Crissy's Dress Down dresses. And she tried some on. The Funky Feathers they thought cool. And the Lip Smacking Good, casual. And the Patchworker, nicely sassy. And the Burlap Bag, really dress down. But they didn't match her mood. So Crissy decided the thing to do was to make her hair short and try her Dress Up rack.

And the very first one she tried on was Very Vanilla and Dina and Brandi and Velvet (and Velvet's little sister, too) all thought Very Vanilla as the very fun thing to wear. They made her put on the Very Vanilla hat. And they were right. It was a very fun outfit to wear. But Crissy said, "You don't wear very fun things when you have a serious problem to talk over with HER." And (as usual) Crissy was right. She slipped on Lemon Lite. Then she put on her Way-Out wig, but thought the combination too light hearted for such a heavy meeting.

Blazering though! Blazering, ah! Blazering was just right! But now her hair? Her Hair! What do you do with her hair? The wig was wrong for Blazering and it went. "But your own hair is too short to go well with Blazering," they said. And it was. And they made her own hair grow (as only Crissy and Velvet and Brandi and Dina, and Velvet's little sister, too, can). They set her hair. They dried her hair. They brushed her hair. And her hair was a very lovely thing to see. So was Crissy. "Now," they said, "you

are ready to talk serious secrets." And she was. And she packed her bag (for a special reason) and she went to see HER. And they laughed, and hugged, and kissed, and said hello (the way good friends will). And Crissy said, "I have something very serious to tell you. I have been very mad, very sad, and very upset." "Why?" SHE cried, "Why Crissy, Why? I don't like to see you upset!" "When you're here," Crissy sighed, "when you're here we laugh and play and try on all my things, and fix my hair, and we talk and sing. But when you go out to places I can't see, I'm all alone with Dina, Brandi, and Velvet (and Velvet's little sister), and I love them all very much. But, it's not the same without you to play with."

"OH!" SHE said, "MY!" SHE said. "Tell me, Crissy, what should I do?" "If," Crissy said, "if only," Crissy said, "when you go out to all those places I can't see and you leave me all alone, if only you would take me, too!" "Yes! Yes! Yes!" SHE laughed. "I will. I will. I will." SHE laughed. "Crissy you're right! From now on I'll take you with me every place I go." And SHE did. And Crissy was never, never mad or sad, or upset anymore. Well, hardly.

And, that was the secret thing Crissy had to say to HER. And that's why she had packed her bag (to be ready to go out with HER).

All you ever have to remember is when you go out, TAKE CRISSY, TOO."

While the grammatically-challenged story is meant for further advertising of other Ideal products, if it encouraged the little girl to carry her Crissy doll around with her everywhere she went, it served another purpose: to advertise the Crissy doll to other people in the general public, too.

A "must-have" for the die-hard Crissy doll collector is the poster that came with some Crissy dolls. The little girl on the poster is disarmingly charming!

Chapter 9

Restorative Methods

Since Crissy® and her friends were play dolls, played with they were. Nevertheless, that doesn't mean that even the most played-with doll isn't able to model all those terrific outfits today. A little elbow grease goes a long way when it comes to these dolls. Just taking the time to comb out her tangles, put a little curl in her hair, clean the vinyl and the eyes, and place a wonderful outfit on a doll produces a valuable and worthwhile addition to a collection. If her hair is totally shot, a Way-out Wig may be in order.

There are some super products on the market that clean clothes with no resulting damage. Products are available, too, for stain removal on vinyl. Always follow the product directions "to the letter" for satisfactory results.

Crissy looks soft and feminine, ready for bed in "The Sleeper Bells" (1969-1970).

Hair Styling

Considering that Crissy and her friends were designed for hair styling play, taking the time to give them each a hair style is very appropriate. If one wishes to have a doll to model each outfit, it is conceivable that there could be quite a few dolls in the group. To keep them from all looking alike, try giving them all different styles.

Most bargain basement dolls that one acquires are going to need a significant amount of work. So let's start with the basics: how to remove tangles in a safe manner that will cause the least amount of hair loss. Undress the doll first. The foundation hair—the short non-growing hair—is the easiest place from which to remove tangles. Using a brush, start near the bottom and work your way up until the hair is smooth. Often, number one, hair-to-the-floor dolls have a "nappiness" to their hair—either on the foundation hair, the 'tail hair, or both. Sometimes, all the brushing in the world will not remove the frizz. In this case, try putting an extremely small amount of mineral oil between your hands. Rub them briskly together. As you work with the hair, it will help tame the frizzies to some extent, but not completely. In this case, it may be necessary simply to create a style that will hide the condition (this will be covered shortly).

As you are smoothing the foundation hair, take note of where the doll's sewn-in part is situated. Separate the part correctly. Mia and Crissy's part is on the left side of their heads. Velvet, Tressy, Brandi, Kerry, Dina, and Cinnamon all have center parts. Cricket has a part on the right side of her head. Tara has no part in her foundation hair.

Note where the part is rooted on each doll.

Brush out tangles in the foundation hair first. Work from the bottom and move up.

All tangles have been removed from this doll's foundation hair.

After taming the foundation hair, it is time to tackle the 'tail. Sometimes this is easier said than done. Yet, with patience, the results can be well worth the time and effort. If the hair is not going to be washed, applying mineral oil to your hands before you work with the doll's hair will give the hair sheen after you are all finished. If the hair is going to be washed, removing all the tangles first is necessary. When brushing out the tangles on the 'tail hair, sit on the floor and lay the doll on her back. Try to separate the 'tail into several small sections: working with a small amount of hair at a time is easier. Smooth each section, brushing from the bottom up to the scalp. After all sections are done, brush the entire 'tail as one section.

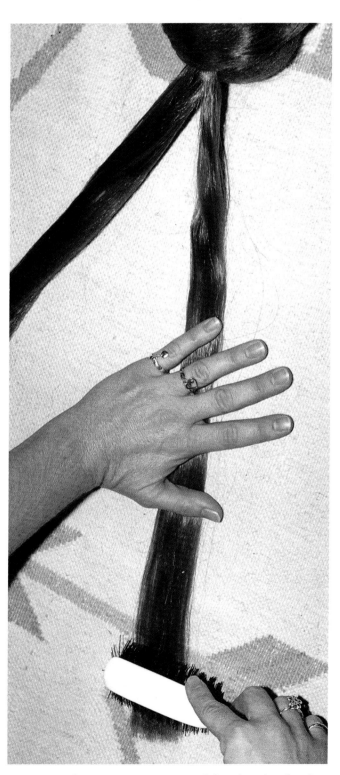

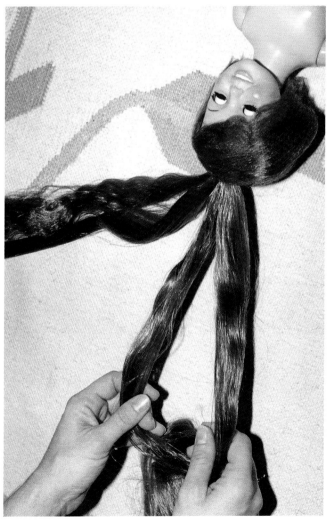

Divide the 'tail in sections.

To remove tangles one section at a time, smooth from the ends and work up toward the scalp.

If the tangles are simply too much to brush out, use a dollop of a balsam hair conditioner on each section of dry hair to facilitate getting a very large-toothed comb through it. At this point, it should be mentioned that human hair conditioners have very little effect on synthetic hair. Conditioners are made to be absorbed into the cuticle layer of human hair, thereby rendering a softer, more pliable condition. Human hair conditioners merely coat synthetic hair. If you put an oily substance on a piece of plastic, it will just sit there. Likewise, putting conditioners on synthetic hair behaves much the same way. It sits there unabsorbed. However, it does have a tendency to attract dirt, dust, and other environmental contaminates when left on synthetic hair. Basically, it won't hurt the hair, but it can cause it to attract these things. Using conditioners to brush out the tangles help to keep the hair soft and more easily worked with in its dry state, but you will need to rinse it out after it has been detangled.

Brush all the 'tail hair at one time after the tangles are removed.

Use a small stream of water so as to not make more tangles after you've removed them.

After detangling, it is time to cleanse the hair. It is a bit difficult to clean the foundation hair without introducing water into the hole where her hair grows, but with diligence, it can be done. It is generally best not to do the foundation hair unless it is necessary. Using the sprayer at the kitchen sink seems to be the easiest way. Wet the 'tail up to one inch from the hole. Any basic soap shampoo (nothing fancy, as her hair is not benefited by conditioning shampoos) is acceptable. Other good products are simple dish washing liquid or Twin Pines of Maine's FORMULA 9-1-1. This makes the hair truly clean without leaving any deposits on it. Do not rub the hair or otherwise move it around too much. Just run the cleansing agent through the 'tail, then rinse thoroughly. Water temperature makes no difference. Wipe downwardly with a dry towel, but do not rub.

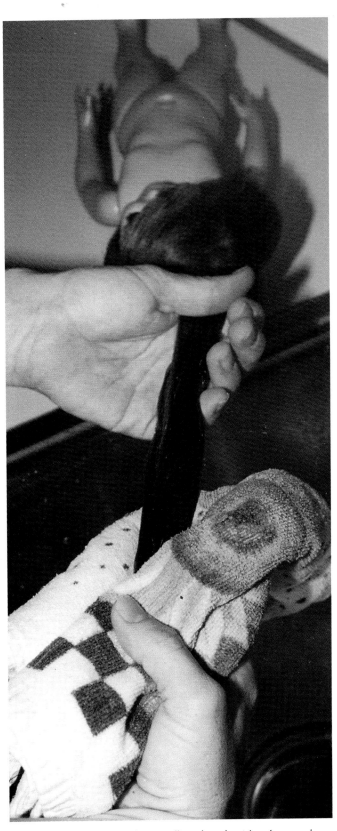

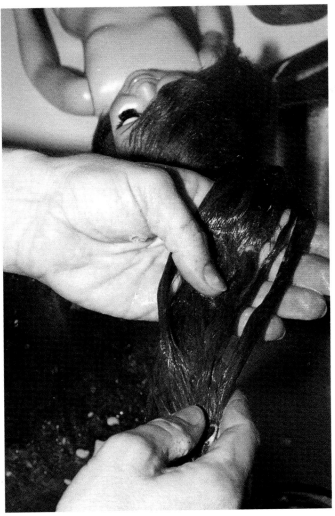

Gently work the cleansing agent through the 'tail, carefully keeping the hair from tangling.

After rinsing the hair, wipe downwardly and gently with a clean towel to remove the excess water.

Now it is time to give the doll a beautiful hair style. Take into consideration the outfit she will be wearing. If it is a formal outfit, a more dressy style will be best. If she is wearing pajamas, beach clothes, or other lounging wear, braids and long flowing tresses look great.

There are two types of hair rollers that work well. Use small pink sponge rollers and end papers for a looser look where the curls will be brushed out. These are very inexpensive at the drugstore or a discount department store, less than $2. Investing in a package is well worth it, especially if you have a large collection. To make sausage curls or tight ringlets, use permanent wave rods and end papers. This kind of curl will not be brushed out. Plan where the rollers will be placed. Decide if the doll will have short hair, long hair, or something in between. A short flip is cute. Tons of tiny braids with the ends tucked into the grow hole have a funky look. Long, luxuriant waves are very formal. A short pageboy is dressy and businesslike.

Previously mentioned was the early kind of Crissy hair (found on very many hair-to-the-floor dolls) that tends to get quite nappy. Black Crissy hair is also made of this very fine type of hair and generally cannot be curled. If this is the case, do not under any circumstances attempt to use the following method to curl it. It melts and shrivels. In fact, you must perform a strand test on every doll before attempting this method. To do this, separate a small portion of the 'tail and dip it into boiling water (not over the stove, as you will risk severe burns and catching the doll on fire). If it shrivels up, do not attempt to go any further. Her hair must be left in an uncurled state. The author or publishing company assumes no responsibility if you ruin your doll.

Now that all the cautions have been stated, it is time to roll the hair. It can be rolled wet or dry, but dry seems to be the easiest. Retract or extend the 'tail to the place you wish it to be. Roll small sections of the 'tail at a time.

Fold end wraps in half and wrap around the hair ends.

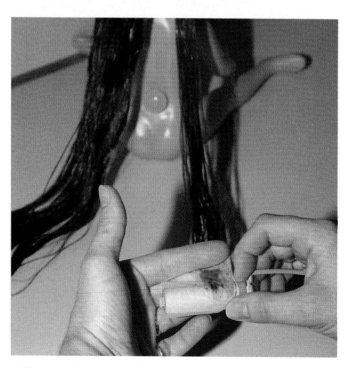

Roll each small section according to the hair style you've selected.

Performing the necessary strand test. Do not skip this step.

Fold an end paper in half, not lengthwise, and put it over the end of the hair strand. Proceed to roll the curler up, either horizontally or vertically, based on the finished style. Start a small pan of boiling water. After the hair is set on the rollers, it is time to wet it with boiling water. A child's "sipper" cup is excellent for this and gives complete control. Thoroughly wet every curler or perm rod. After this is accomplished, spray each curler with cold water. This helps bring it back to a cool temperature very quickly. Have small towels on standby. Wrap the doll's head in a towel and gently squeeze out the excess water. Take the rollers down. It is not necessary to wait until it is dry. In fact, waiting days and days for it to dry usually causes the hair to get "stinky" since it takes so long. The results between taking it down dry or wet are the same anyway. Using heat to reform the shape of plastic or other synthetic product is unaffected by whether it is wet or dry.

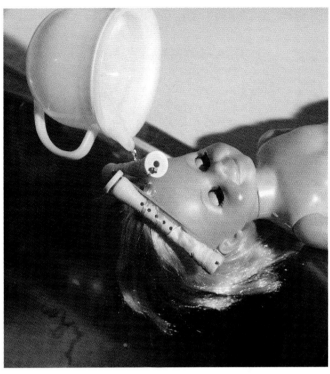

Using boiling water to replace Velvet's corkscrew curls.

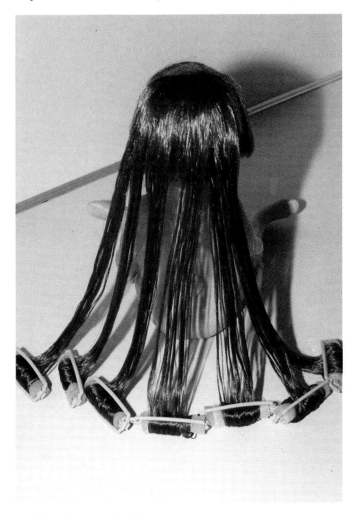

Rolled and awaiting the boiling water.

To help avoid tangles, try wrapping the rollers up in tulle, then wetting the rollers with the water.

Dousing rollers with cold water reforms the synthetic hair immediately.

Gently squeeze out the excess water with a clean towel.

The curly results.

If you have set ringlets or sausage curls, use a wire pick to put them in place. Let the doll's hair dry, then dress her. If she is to have softer curls, use the pick to style her hair while wet. A small amount of non-lacquer hair spray is acceptable after it has dried, but do try not to get it on the doll's face and certainly not on her clothes.

Some points that cannot be stressed enough are that the hair must be tested before you proceed with the boiling water method of hair curling. Early hair-to-the-floor Crissy dolls and most black dolls have very fine hair that cannot withstand the heat of boiling water. Also, human hair conditioners produce only marginal results on synthetic hair, and leaving too much conditioner residue attracts dust and dirt. The use of hair spray is appropriate if used sparingly and if you do not plan to change the style. If hair spray is used, the hair would need to be washed in order to be restyled.

This sweet little Velvet had to endure a dastardly haircut at the hands of her little owner. To hide her handiwork, Velvet's 'tail was retracted completely into her head. Then the foundation hair was curled under, and the remaining 'tail was wrapped in permanent wave rods and submitted to the boiling water method of hair setting. One would have to agree that what was once a useless doll, now looks darling!

Crissy looks soft and feminine, ready for bed in "The Sleeper Bells" (1969-1970).

There is nothing more beautiful than a nice Velvet with the corkscrew curls recurled and the hard curl at the end of her 'tail replaced.

Vinyl Cleaning

Little children loved their Crissy dolls! Happily, most grow-hair dolls were played with to the point that they simply need some clean-up work. Nevertheless, you will occasionally come across one that needs a major overhaul. Crissy and her friends were made of different kinds of vinyls and plastics. To clean the vinyl, one only needs to assemble a few basic items: a soft toothbrush, a soft cloth, FORMULA 9-1-1 by Twin Pines of Maine, towels, and a sink. The kitchen counter is a wonderful work area. FORMULA 9-1-1 is a great product for removing basic dirt from a doll, and it also removes crayon, lipstick, tar, gum, tape, and other sticky residues and wax. It is gentle and smells great! Some like to use it for cleaning the doll's hair, too.

Use the soft toothbrush to apply a small amount of cleaner to soiled areas of the doll. Then use a clean damp cloth to wipe away the grime. Clean small areas at a time. Some find it helpful to pin the doll's hair out of the way before cleaning the doll.

If the doll is stained with ink or other stains absorbed into the vinyl, try using Twin Pines' REMOVE-ZIT. This product works well on the soft vinyl arms. The body is blow-molded plastic, as are the legs. Sometimes, it does not work well on this type of plastic. It is always recommended to do a patch test on every doll, on every part whether arm or leg when you use REMOVE-ZIT. Put a very small dollop of the product on an inconspicuous location. Wait the prescribed amount of time (always follow directions to the T). If it does not work well, then you may be able to hide the stain with a shoe, a long sleeve, or pants leg. Be aware that the product does remove face paint. Faces can be repainted, so it may be worth it to remove major stains from a face. When cleaning a face, pin the hair up with hair pins. Using a very small cat's tongue paintbrush, paint the REMOVE-ZIT around the eye paint and the lips. Go nearly up to the lip paint, but not on it. The whole facial area needs to be done, not just a stain. Otherwise, you will end up with a very clean spot if only one small place is cleaned with the product. Try also to avoid getting the product on the doll's neck stem. This is blow-molded plastic.

REMOVE-ZIT works very nicely on the vinyl shoes. White shoes clean the best. When removing stains from shoes and boots with color, the whole shoe needs to be cleaned as it removes some of the original color. A shoe lighter in color is better than a shoe with a stain. Both shoes will need to be done so that the pair will match. Be patient if it takes a week or more of applying and reapplying the product. In reality, the product works in a short period of time.

Sometimes, you will find that you can clean a doll only as well as she can be cleaned without damaging her, and then simply cover any stained or damaged parts with clothing. Fortunately, that is not often. Even if you do need to cover a damaged Crissy's flaw with a long sleeve or pants leg, since there are so many different outfits to choose from, it shouldn't be difficult to have your Crissy looking fab and stylish.

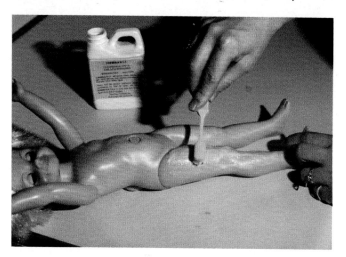

Velvet is getting cleaned up. This is the doll with the severe haircut pictured on page 89.

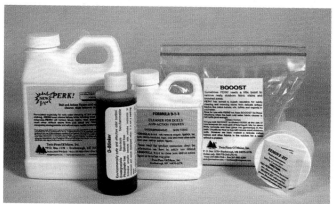

Eye Cleaning

Surely, there are a few collectors out there who've seen a grow-hair girl afflicted by the "disease" of white eye mold. When the mold is white, the good news is that is easily removable. Scrape out a majority of it with a tooth-pick that has the tip flattened. (Biting on the end a few times will flatten it!) Then *slightly* dampen a soft tooth-brush and put a very small amount of vinyl cleaner on it. Rub it around to make sure it is nearly dry to the touch. Clean the eyelid and the pupil area with the toothbrush. Avoid wetting the brush. Introducing water into the eye will initiate rusting. Clean off the eyelid and inner eye with a clean, *slightly* dampened washcloth to remove the cleaner. If water inadvertently gets into the eye, allow the doll to lie face down on a towel for a few hours to allow the water to drain out. Rust in the eye is very unsightly and impossible to remove.

Many collectors, and doll dealers, too, recommend the introduction of certain oils into the eyes of many kinds of dolls. Unfortunately, this is not always a good idea, especially with the grow-hair girls. Some oils "gum up" with age and will cause further damage later on. Rest assured that by simply cleaning the eyes gently, your girl will see well for a long time!

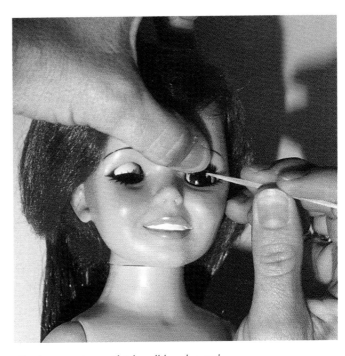

Continue scraping until it has all been loosened.

A flattened toothpick is a wonderful tool for chiseling out that nasty white eye mold.

Gently brush out the residue from the white eye mold.

Repainting

Ideal face paint has fabulous resiliency. Rarely does one find a doll with damaged face paint. Even if a doll has been played with to the point that she is missing some paint here and there, take heart, she can be fixed.

Assemble a very small fine point paintbrush, multi-purpose acrylic paint—in carnation pink for lips and medium brown for eyelashes—fabric medium, and a small plate at a convenient worktable. The acrylic paint comes in small two-ounce bottles as does the fabric medium. The fabric medium acts as a fixative of sorts: it keeps the acrylic paint from flaking off. It is also removable and does no permanent damage to the vinyl face of the doll. To remove it, scrub briskly with a soft toothbrush. Use caution with other types of paints. Some types will eventually bleed into the surrounding vinyl where repainted. If this is already the case with previous repainting, it can be cleaned off with Twin Pines' REMOVE-ZIT.

To repaint features, place a small amount of paint on the plate, then stir in three times as much of the fabric medium. Using the fine paintbrush, repaint the lips or eye makeup. Admittedly, this takes practice. One may have to paint, remove, and repaint again until it works. The paint is of a runny consistency due to the addition of the fabric medium. However, this yields a very smooth finish after the paint has dried. If the mixed paint appears too light in color, don't worry; it will dry darker. After it is completely dry, a second coat may look best.

Preparing paint for Crissy's lips.

New lipstick for Crissy!

Clothing Care

Blush that has worn off or been "cleaned" off can be replaced with an inexpensive powder blush in hot pink. Surprisingly, hot pink looks very authentic on Crissy and friends. One thing to watch for is the addition of mica to the powder blush. Mica will cause little shiny flecks to appear on the vinyl. This is unacceptable. Most high-end department stores have a very nice selection of blushes at their makeup counters. A hot pink blush designed for women with dark skin looks very nice on Crissy. The pigments in the blush will eventually be absorbed into the vinyl and will become unremovable.

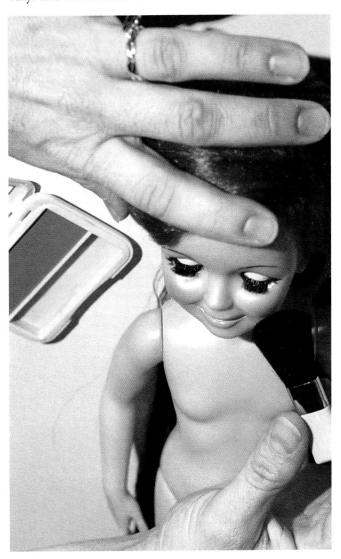

Replacing faded blush on a number one Crissy.

To prolong the life of vintage doll clothes, one should use caution and common sense. Some items should never be used such as chlorine bleach or harsh denture cleaning chemicals. Bleach breaks down natural fibers, especially when the fabric has aged for awhile. One may wish to use gentle cleaners designed for delicate fabrics, and cold water for simply cleaning years of dust out of the clothing items. Sometimes, though, one has to get tough on tough dirt. A good overnight soak in Twin Pines' PERK! cleans most items well. If the clothing item has high color to it, it is usually best to fill a sink with ice water, the prescribed amount of PERK! and then let the item soak for a few hours, adding ice as necessary. This keeps the colors from bleeding out, but hot water encourages it. Rinse very well in cold water and lay flat to dry on clean, white absorbent towels.

For whites and light-colored garments, such as undies or yellow cotton dresses, the addition of Twin Pines' BOOOST! to the PERK! makes them bright and clean. It is especially good for tough stains. Be careful with garments with high color, though, as color bleeding may take place.

After the clothing items are cleaned, think carefully about ironing them. Most vintage items should not be ironed, but lightly steamed, instead, on a model doll used only for that purpose. Garments of cotton can be ironed on a low setting. A doll-sized ironing board is indispensable for a collector with a large collection.

Common sense will tell most people that some items cannot be washed with water. "The Turned On Mini," made of eyelash lamé, must not be cleaned at all. This type of fabric cannot be dry-cleaned, nor washed with water. Several items, such as the taffeta skirt and red velvet blazers of Velvet and Crissy's "Blazering" outfits, must be dry-cleaned. Velvet's very early white lace pantsuit, with the deep purple velvet ribbon on it, cannot be washed with water, as the ribbon will bleed *profusely* onto the lace. Velvet's "Checker Check" taffeta dress also needs to be dry-cleaned. Be sure that the dry-cleaning service is insured against the loss of a valuable vintage doll garment before you leave the establishment. Make it clear that they will be held responsible. If they refuse to be responsible, find another establishment. If in doubt of the appropriate cleaning method, research the fabric. Find something in your closet that is of a similar fabric and read that label. A good rule of thumb: if in doubt, don't.

When ironing out wrinkles and creases, it is best to use extreme caution. Some fabrics simply cannot be ironed. The wedding gowns are made of a synthetic satin that does not withstand the heat of an iron. In fact, all synthetic Ideal clothing should never be ironed. Try investing in an inexpensive travel steamer, if you won't be using it for much more than your doll collection. It is nice to have since it works best with small jobs like doll clothing. Keep a "beater" doll in your closet to wear the clothes while they are being steamed out.

A cotton garment irons well with a regular iron on a low setting. Be mindful of small plastic buttons and synthetic laces that may melt. Once a piece of clothing is ruined, there is no going back.

After your doll has been cleaned, her hair has been styled, and she is dressed in a new outfit, she is ready for all the admiring glances she is bound to get!

But what happens when one gets items by purchasing a collection or box lot that are too far gone for any use? A true die-hard collector hates to see anything go to waste. For instance, one collector found a case that came with a box lot of clothes and was in a dilapidated state. There was no handle, no snaps, and large tears. Using a new pattern for a backpack, she fashioned a novel, one-of-a-kind backpack that is fun to look at and a wonderful conversation starter at doll shows and sales!

What about the shoes that have seen better days? If the straps have been broken off, try cutting out the toe area of the shoe a bit farther down with fingernail scissors. Then, using jewel glue (for adhering faux gems and jewels

to garments), attach ribbon bows in a matching color. This idea can be seen in Chapter 10 on a Velvet doll wearing a red gingham coverall set. This just goes to show, there is a use for everything.

Please note: The information on products and methods suggested previously are given in good faith. Using common sense and following package directions are paramount to good results. However, the author, nor the publisher, are responsible for damage done to the doll while attempting restorative methods. Now, have fun!

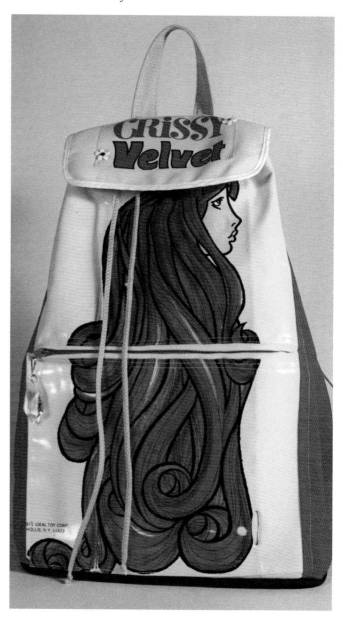

A rescued Crissy case that was unusable turns into a nifty backpack! There's a use for everything!

Chapter 10

Other Growing Hair Dolls
and Related Items

Some people say that there are a couple of things in life on which one can depend: death and taxes. This is probably true. Another thing that can be depended on is that eventually all big sellers are capitalized on, a true fact indeed. A certain big-selling soft drink has been copied. So has the 11-1/2-inch fashion doll idea. This list of American products that have been copied is endless.

The Crissy® doll and her friends are no different. Following the success of the grow-hair girls, big department stores produced new clothing lines for them. Toy manufacturers offered new cases for their fashions, some even larger and more elaborate than Ideal's. The dolls themselves were mimicked, even to the point of having growing hair—though their hair-growing mechanisms did not operate in the same way as Crissy's. (The mechanics involved in making Crissy's hair grow were patented.)

These are the middle-sized members of the Dolly Surprise family of dolls. They came in many different outfits and hair colors.

Grow-hair dolls

1970: VALERIE, With Growin' Pretty Hair, stock #3164, Mattel

Mattel's entry in the grow-hair doll race was a darling doll named Valerie. With very blonde hair and painted blue eyes, Valerie is adorable in her white dress with yellow lace overlay. She also wears white panties, white anklets, and white shoes. The face mold that Mattel used was a very commonly used mold that they used for at least a dozen dolls. She has an opened mouth with four teeth showing. In keeping with the hair play theme, hair rollers, a brush, and a comb were packed in the box with her.

Her hair-growing mechanism is quite unique. As the long 'tail is pulled, it catches on a clutch of sorts, holding it out at the desired length. To make the 'tail go back in, one has only to give it a slight tug. Valerie's non-growing hair is tied up in a topknot with a yellow ribbon, and a cute little lock of hair curls over her forehead at one temple. This doll looks very juvenile compared to Crissy's sophistication. Her height and looks are more comparable with Velvet and the younger girls.

1971: Kim, Uneeda

Uneeda Doll Company of Brooklyn jumped on the grow-hair doll bandwagon, too. At 5 inches tall, Kim may be the smallest grow-hair doll ever made. Kim was sold with a small wardrobe of clothing, which included a bridal gown, a minidress, and a slacks set. Curlers, a comb, and a brush were sold with her, too. The whole set was issued in a small, red vinyl case.

Kim's foundation hair is rather curly, and she has a non-growing ponytail right behind her grow-hair hole. A very simple mechanism causes her 'tail to grow. The base of the tail is attached to a length of elastic, which is threaded through the inside of the doll and anchored to the bottom of her foot. This device pulls the 'tail in, retracting it to its shorter length. To make the 'tail long, the little stylist slips a bead cemented to the base of the 'tail through a slit at the top of the doll's head. The bead prevents the 'tail from retracting, holding Kim's hair to its longer length. Because of this rather simple method, Kim's hair can be only two lengths, either long or short.

Not a formidable foe in the grow-hair market in the 1970s was Valerie. She had a look all her own.

Uneeda's Kim was a minor entry in the grow-hair doll contest. This doll was also sold with the name "Dana," in a small box.

1972: Miss Deb, with Hair that Grows Longer, stock #61620, Uneeda

The auburn-haired Miss Deb doll was maybe the closest copy of an actual Crissy doll that was ever produced. Interestingly, on the back of the box, major reference was made to the fact that this doll was copyrighted. The notice of copyright warned that any copying, reproduction, manufacture, or sale without the authorization of Uneeda constituted an infringement of copyright. This was written in big, bold black letters.

Miss Deb has a superfluous amount of foundation hair. However, her 'tail is quite sparse. The doll's hair-growing mechanism operates in a rather simple manner, like the previously mentioned Kim doll's. The base of the 'tail is attached to a length of elastic, which is in turn anchored inside the doll to a grommet at the base of her right foot. To keep the 'tail from retracting, a bead cemented to the base of the 'tail can be pulled outside of the doll through a slit at the top of her head. The bead (and the 'tail) can't go back into her head then. To make the hair go back in, just slide the bead out of the slit and her 'tail moves rather quickly back to short. Like Kim, Miss Deb's 'tail can be only in or out, making her hair either short or long.

Miss Deb was issued in several hair colors and clothing styles. She was sold only at Grants Department Stores. As inexpensively as she appears to have been made, it is obvious that she was little competition for Crissy and friends. The box deserves an honorable mention, though. The hand-drawn figure of Miss Deb is almost a perfect copy of the hand-drawn Crissy profile decorating the earliest boxes.

The doll molds were used for another doll called Magic Meg, with Hair that Grows Longer, stock # 30616. She was also produced by Uneeda. She however, was not a Grant's store exclusive.

The low-quality Miss Deb doll was a Grant's department store exclusive.

1987-1990: The Dolly Surprise Series, Playskool

Riding in on the tail end of the grow-hair doll success (Country Crissy was offered from 1982-1983), Dolly Surprise was successful because the concept of a grow-hair doll, historically speaking, did well. This entire series of durably made dolls was well executed, and each doll wore very nice clothing.

The series came in different sizes. The Little Miss Dolly Surprise, who stands 6-1/2 inches tall, was issued in black or white, in one of nine different outfits. She came with a comb and a storybook. To shorten Dolly's hair, one has only to put her right arm down at her side and move her left arm up and down. To make her hair longer, raise her right arm. This activates a spring tension "motor" that releases her short hair, and makes it long again. Her grow hair is crimped.

The 10-1/2-inch Dolly Surprise operates in the same manner. This size was also released in countless clothing styles and hair colors, and she also came in black and white issues. Some of the dolls of this size have a cute plastic butterfly sitting on their heads. Some do not. Her 'tail is also crimped.

The big, 14-inch sized Dolly Surprise was issued as a little girl doll and as a baby doll. The little girl version, the Head-to-Toe Dolly Surprise, has hair that grows right to her toes! What a great idea! The Baby Dolly Surprise's hair doesn't grow quite that long. Both dolls' grow-hair mechanisms operate in the same way that all Dolly Surprise series dolls do.

Playskool kept the doll series interesting by offering play sets, such as the Dolly Surprise Beauty Parlor for the 10-1/2-inch dolls, and packaged outfits, too.

Top: A surprise hit was the Dolly Surprise series of dolls by Playskool. These are the smallest of the family.

Bottom: The biggest family members were this Baby Dolly Surprise and Head-to-Toe Dolly Surprise.

Extra outfits, interesting accessories, and dolls that did different things (like this one that sunburns) kept interest going for awhile with the doll-buying public.

Clothing

Just as toy and doll companies make clothing to fit popular dolls today, extensive clothing lines were created for the fashion dolls of the 1970s. Crissy and her friends not only had their own collection of Ideal-made clothes, but Sears, Penney's, and Wards department store catalogs offered collections for them, too.

These four Velvet dolls look adorable in their 1973 Wards toy catalog outfits.

This outfit was offered in the 1973 JC Penney's toy catalog.

Some non-Ideal outfits are rather unique, such as this impressive leopard print pantsuit. It was made to fit Velvet (as stated on the package) and is embellished with a "pearl" necklace, fringy scarf, and an ID bracelet.

More non-Ideal outfits: one would be hard-pressed to find another doll that could wear these outfits so perfectly.

Above: This denim pantsuit must have been popular, as it turns up very frequently on Crissy dolls and in box lots.

Far Left: This outfit was packaged rather inexpensively, but it was definitely made for Crissy.

Left: Totsy's Funtime Fashions mentions, on the label, that Beautiful Crissy can wear its clothes.

These outfits weren't as well made, and they really didn't offer the high style that Crissy was used to having, but they were convenient to purchase along with the grow-hair girl that was offered on the same catalog page. It is curious that Ideal outfits were sometimes not even pictured in these catalogs. Once in awhile, the catalog pages presented their version of a grow-hair doll right alongside the Ideal girls. Even non-Ideal hair care sets were sold on the same page.

Several dolls have appeared at doll shows and flea markets wearing some of these outfits. Usually, they fit quite nicely and can be considered valuable additions to a grow-hair doll collection. So, before casting off an outfit of questionable origin, it may be a good idea to put it away for safe keeping until it can be identified with a toy catalog of that era. The catalog pages illustrated in Chapter 11 of this book, for example, depict the grow-hair girls modeling outfits made by a variety of other manufacturers, and may help you identify them.

Even Velvet-sized clothes were made.

Some of the outfits were rather understated, but some were stylish.

Cases

Examples of doll cases, rather large ones, have surfaced that were obvious attempts to capitalize on the grow-hair doll craze. Many of them are just plain wonderful. Various companies made them. The compartments usually accommodated a tall doll and several outfits, and had drawers and bins for shoes, hats, and incidentals. The graphics will indicate the era the case was made if the case is not marked with a copyright date.

The Hi-style Doll Case by Miner Industries, New York City, is an example of just such a case. This big case is 21 inches tall, bigger than Ideal's cases. The ultra-mod graphics feature flowers, butterflies, clouds, and a happy girl wearing bell-bottom slacks. There is no date on this case, but it was acquired with a Look Around Crissy inside and clothes from the year that doll was issued, 1972. This would seem to be an accurate date considering the graphics on the front. Miner Industries made other doll cases as well.

After securing all the cases that were originally produced for the dolls by Ideal, it is a natural progression for serious collectors to seek out these marvelous additions to their collections.

The fun-looking Hi-style Doll Case by Miner Industries is a groovy addition to the collection.

This Miner Industries case was offered alongside the grow-hair girls in most of the Wards toy catalogs of the era. Just how groovy can you get?

Chapter 11

Department Store Catalog Pages

BEAUTIFUL CRISSY
the famous doll
with hair that "grows"

Only **5⁷⁷** *when you buy*
her 5-outfit wardrobe, too!
Crissy **6⁶⁶** *separately*

[1] **Crissy is an exquisite beauty** with delicately tinted features, lifelike vinyl head and arms, lovely deepset open-and-close eyes. Her luxurious rooted hair can be combed and styled, made to "grow" from short to long. She can stand alone or be posed gracefully. Wears mini dress, panties, high-style shoes. Abt. 17½ in. tall.
48 G 10200—Crissy doll only. Ship. wt. 1 lb. 11 oz....**6.66**

FABULOUS VALUE. Crissy is only 5.77 when you buy her in combination with stylish outfits, (2) below!
48G10247—Crissy plus Outfits. Ship. wt. 2 lbs. 4 oz. **11.76**

FABULOUS VALUE

5 Outfits for 17½-18-in. Dolls 5⁹⁹ set

[2] **Stylish wardrobe** for Crissy, Brandi or Aimée (opp. page). For all occasions: hot pants ensemble, nightie, wrap-around long skirt with pants, slacks with long tunic, mini dress with stretch tights. *Dolls not included.*
48 G 11012—Ship. wt. 9 oz....................set 5.99

The World of Crissy

"Look Around" Velvet and Crissy
Your choice 7⁷⁷

[3] [4] More **FABULOUS VALUES**. Glamorous "growing-hair" dolls seen on TV, now more realistic than ever. Their heads turn to look around and their bodies move and twist like real models. Just pull the string in their backs—no batteries needed. Lifelike vinyl heads and arms, open-and-close eyes, posable jointed bodies, rooted hair that grows. Buy them extra outfits at left.
(3) **Look Around Velvet** in short plaid taffeta, slippers.
48 G 10243—Abt. 15 in. tall. Ship. wt. 1 lb. 13 oz....**7.77**
(4) **Look Around Crissy** in long plaid taffeta, slippers.
48 G 10242—Abt. 17½ in. tall. Ship. wt. 1 lb. 15 oz...**7.77**

Boots 'n Shoes 1⁷⁷ set

[5] **Two pairs each**, boots, shoes. Asst'd. colors. Wt. 10 oz.
For Crissy and Brandi.
48 G 11014.............set 1.77
For Velvet and Dina.
48 G 11015.............set 1.77

5 Outfits for 15-in. Dolls 4⁹⁹ set

[6] **Stylish wardrobe** for Velvet, Dina or other fashion dolls. For all occasions: hot pants ensemble with skirt, pajamas, shift and shorts set, jumper style dress, 3-pc. poncho set. *Dolls not included.*
48 G 11013—Ship. wt. 9 oz...................set 4.99

New friends!
Dina and Brandi

[9] [10] **Beautiful new "growing hair" friends** from California with glowing tan skin and sun-kissed golden hair. They're the same size as popular Velvet and Crissy, can wear the same clothes. And their lovely hair "grows" the same way, too! Lifelike vinyl heads and arms, rooted hair. Jointed bodies with swivel waists. They can stand alone or be posed gracefully.
(9) **Dina** in lavender swimsuit, tie-up clogs. Butterfly tattoo.
48 G 10245—Abt. 15 in. tall. Ship. wt. 1 lb. 8 oz....**5.97**
(10) **Brandi** in burnt-orange swimsuit, knee-laced clogs.

Tote Case 4⁹⁹

[7] **Take Crissy** or her friends on outings. White vinyl-covered case about 21 in. high, has molded handle, closing clasp. Space for doll and outfits. *Doll and clothing*

Hair Care Set 3²⁹

[8] **Everything you need** to set and style fashion dolls' hair! Rollers, clips, pins, comb, brush, barrettes, side combs, yarn ties plus shampoo, conditioner, compact, mirror. Vinyl snap-bag for keeping it all together!

An incredible selection of non-Ideal clothing was featured in the Wards centennial Christmas catalog of 1972.

17-inch tall Crissy has hair that "grows" from a short flip to a floor length cascade

4-piece Gift Set $12⁹⁹

1 Crissy with the wide, wide go-to-sleep eyes and thick, shiny hair. She's a dream of a beauty queen. Press her tummy to make her hair grow . . turn the knob on her back to make it short again. Hair is rooted, so you can comb, brush, and set it. Vinyl Crissy wears a lace party dress, panties, shoes. Her formal-length organza gown is trimmed with marabou feathers. Hair-styling booklet, comb included.
49 C 30748—Shpg. wt. 1 lb. 12 oz. Set $12.99

2 Pajamas, quilted robe with lace trim.
49 C 30752—Shpg. wt. 5 oz. $3.99

3 Hooded cape with fur-look trim, pompons.
49 C 30751—Shpg. wt. 5 oz. $3.99
Note: Dolls not included with outfits.

4 Hair Care Kit. Incl. all setting, styling needs.
49 C 30749—Shipping weight 6 oz. $1.99

MINIATURE DOLLS

4-inch tall Pee Wee and Baby Pee Wee $4⁹⁹
Two wee vinyl tots with go-everywhere wardrobes of 3 extra outfits for each. They travel in their own plastic steamer trunk with dresser, hangers. Or fit in your pocket. 4 inches tall with 1-piece body, turning head, rooted hair you can comb. Baby Pee Wee drinks 'n wets, too.
49 C 30742—Shpg. wt. 14 oz. Set $4.99

5-inch tall Tiny Teen with trunk and clothes $4⁹⁹
The tiniest teen in town is a real fashion plate. Likes to change clothes so often that she travels with her own plastic steamer trunk with dresser and 6 outfits, hangers. 5 inches tall; rooted hair; long eyelashes; vinyl body you can bend and pose. Comes dressed in a lovely bridal gown and veil.
49 C 30741—Shpg. wt. 1 lb. . . . . Set $4.99

2½-inch PETAL PEOPLE

Petals open—these cuties lift out, bend and pose

Petals close—to keep them safe the whole night through

Each $1⁹⁹

Each vinyl pixie has rooted hair; "lives" in a 12-in. tall plastic flower and pot.
(5) 49C30127—Rosy Rose
(6) 49C3013—Daffi Dill
(7) 49C30129—Sunny Flower
(8) 49C30131-Dizzy Daisy
(9) 49C30128-Polly Poppy
(10) 49C30126-Tiny Tulip
Wt. ea. 10 oz. Each $1.99

5 Rosy Rose
6 Daffi Dill
7 Sunny Flower
8 Dizzy Daisy
9 Polly Poppy
10 Tiny Tulip

Chubby little Nana, our Italian baby

She looks so real, so adorable . . 6 inches tall

11 You'll fall in love with her rosy cheeks, dimpled hands, little legs with their creases of baby fat. Vinyl; rooted hair.
49 C 30755—Wt. 8 oz. $2.49

12 Knit slacks, jacket, hat.
49 C 30765—Wt. 5 oz. $1.99

13 Knit slacks, hooded cape.
49 C 30766—Wt. 5 oz. $1.99

14 Canopy Bed. Frame, mattress, canopy and spread.
49 C 30767—Wt. 12 oz. $2.99
Complete Set. Includes doll, 2 extra outfits, canopy bed.
49 C 30759-Wt. 1 lb. 14 oz. $8.99

Doll not included with outfits

604 Sears PCBKM AEDSLG

This page from a 1969 Sears catalog shows the number one Crissy with her Sears exclusive marabou gown.

Glamour Dolls

Vinyl Fashion Tote 3⁸⁸

Take Crissy or Velvet or Joann on trips. Colorful vinyl-covered case about 20 in. high; molded handle, quilted lining. Space for doll and her outfits (not included).
48 T 11517—Wt. 2 lbs. 9 oz.....3.88

Big Hair-Care Set 2⁹⁸

Styling kit for Crissy, Joann, Velvet, other dolls. Rollers, pins, clips, comb, brush, barrettes, side combs, yarn ties, shampoo, conditioner; compact, mirror. Drawstring bag.
48 T 11757—Ship. wt. 12 oz.....2.98

Set of 5 Fashion Outfits for Crissy 5⁹⁹

Let Crissy hit the scene in latest styles: maxi coat, flippy skimmer, bell-bottom pantsuit, A-line jumper, "at home" maxi. (Dolls not included.)
48 T 11024—Wards Special Outfits. Ship. wt. 10 oz.....set 5.99

Set of 5 Outfits for Joann or Velvet 4⁹⁹

All-occasion fashions: pantsuit with poncho, swing tunic and tights, leisure-wear maxi, halter-top bell bottoms, kicky skimmer. (Dolls not included.)
48 T 11025—Wards Special Outfits. Ship. wt. 9 oz.....set 4.99

Beautiful Crissy—in new satin mini dress 9⁹⁹ 18-in.

1 Exquisite beauty has delicately tinted features, flesh-like vinyl head and arms, lovely deep-set dark eyes that open and close. Her luxurious rooted hair can be combed and styled, made to "grow" from a short bob to a romantic flowing sweep. She can stand alone or be posed in graceful ways. Wears stylish mini dress, matching panties, high style shoes.
48 T 10200—Crissy with hairbrush. Ship. wt. 1 lb. 9 oz.....9.99

Joann, a charming young friend for Crissy 7⁸⁸ 15 in.

2 A blond beauty whose wonderful rooted hair can be made long or short, and styled in all sorts of attractive ways. Sparkling blue open and close eyes, vinyl head and hands, tinted features. Can stand alone or be posed. Wears smart red mini-length jumper dress, panties, socks and shoes.
48 T 10202—Joann with comb. Ship. wt. 1 lb. 4 oz.....7.88

Velvet, Crissy's adorable new cousin 9⁴⁹ 16 in.

3 Velvet resembles her famous cousin in beauty and style. Glistening blond rooted hair can be combed, set, made to grow from short to knee-length tresses. Has violet open and close eyes, vinyl head and hands, tinted features. Can stand alone or be posed. Purple velvet mini dress, panties, shoes.
48 T 10201—Velvet with hairbrush. Ship. wt. 1 lb. 8 oz.....9.49

SAVE THIS CATALOG!
Order toys from this book until August 31, 1971.

FABULOUS VALUE

Missy

A pretty lass with her own wardrobe...exclusive at Wards

Only 4⁹⁹ 16 in.

A wonderful playmate—it's such fun to style her hair and change her clothes! She's fully jointed, can stand alone. Has lifelike vinyl head, lovely brown eyes that open and close. Long flip hair-do is rooted, can be combed and set. Wears groovy mod mini dress, panties, socks, shoes. With slacks, blouse, 2 dresses.
48 T 11868—Ship. wt. 1 lb. 6 oz.....4.99

Beautiful Crissy . . . with hair that "grows!"

The glamorous doll you've seen on TV has a new cousin, Velvet, and a new friend, Joann. Their hair grows, too!

ALL WARDS 325

This Wards catalog page shows 1970-issue dolls, but the toys were available until August 1971. It's curious how Wards pushed their grow-hair doll, Joann, right alongside Crissy and Velvet. Other outfits for the grow-hair girls were sold on this page, too.

The Movin' Groovin' Group

15-inch dolls with twist-turn waists.. swing their shoulders around and their long hair tosses from side to side

1 Velvet looks so pretty and poseable, she almost seems alive. She has sparkling eyes, silky hair that grows to her waist and smooth vinyl skin. She's 15 in. tall, jointed, and all dressed up in a ruffled mini party dress.
Shpg. wt. 1 lb. 8 oz.
49 C 35101 . . . . $8.44

2 Cricket loves to model and pose.. and no wonder! Isn't she lovely with her bright eyes, creamy vinyl skin and shiny hair that grows to her waist. She's wearing a mod mini dress. 15 in. tall. Jointed.
Shpg. wt. 1 lb. 8 oz.
49 C 35103 . . . . $8.44

1 Movin' Groovin' Velvet $8.44

2 Movin' Groovin' Cricket $8.44

MIA by Ideal

She's 15 in. tall $6.97

Mia's coming to play with you all dressed in a sporty playsuit. She has beautiful hair that grows to her waist; jointed vinyl body.
Shpg. wt. 1 lb. 6 oz.
49 C 35097 . . . . $6.97

17½-inch beauties by Ideal

3 **4**

EACH $7.97

(3 and 4) So pretty.. with their delicate features and cascading hair. They have smooth vinyl skin, big bright eyes and growing hair. Fully jointed; 17½ in. tall. Shpg. wt. ea. 1 lb. 6 oz.

3 Kerry.. dressed for play in a perky play set.
49 C 35098 . . . . $7.97

4 Tressy.. all dressed up in a high-fashion mini.
49 C 35122 . . . . $7.97

Shoe Wardrobe

$1.89

For Cricket, Velvet and Mia. Includes 2 pairs of shoes and 2 pairs of long boots.
Shipping weight 5 oz.
49 C 31164 . . . . $1.89

10 Sears PCBKW AEDG

The 1971 grow-hair dolls offered by Sears.

GROWS..

For Tressy, Crissy and Kerry $2.94 each

Change their hairdos from a short bob to luxuriously long. Just press each doll's tummy, pull her hair and watch it "grow". A knob on her back winds it short again

Hair Dryer with bonnet, hose .. it really works

$2.99 without batteries

For any Ideal "growing hair" doll. (Doll not incl.) Actually blows air. Plastic. Uses 2 "AA" batteries, order pkg. below. Wt. 1 lb. 8 oz.
49 C 31177 .. **$2.99**

"AA" Batteries.
Pkg. of 6. Wt. 6 oz.
49 C 8402—Pkg. 99c

1 Hob Nobbler . . 2-pc. maxi suit.
49 C 31166—Wt. 7 oz **$2.94**

2 Grape Drape . . a swingin' suit with dress, coat and scarf.
49 C 31167—Shpg. wt. 7 oz. . . **$2.94**

3 Drenched Trench . . midi-length raincoat with scarf.
49 C 31169—Shpg. wt. 7 oz. . . **$2.94**

4 Jean Machine . . mod pants, tunic, sweater and belt.
49 C 31171—Shpg. wt. 7 oz. . . **$2.94**

5 The Snuggler . . hooded maxi.
49 C 31172—Shpg. wt. 7 oz. **$2.94**

6 Surf's Up . . a bright bathing outfit with long beach coat.
49 C 31168—Shpg. wt. 7 oz. **$2.94**

NOTE: Dolls, shoes not incl. with outfits above

Shoe Wardrobe $1.89 set

For Crissy, Tressy or Kerry . . 2 pair of shoes, 2 pair of long boots.
49 C 31165—Wt. 8 oz . . . Set **$1.89**

Hair Setting Kit $3.49 without battery

"Curler warmer" with 8 rollers and accessories . . great for any Ideal "growing hair" doll. Includes "hair spray", comb, brush, "mirror", hair decorations and more . . even a handy styling booklet. Plastic "warmer" lights curlers with a soft glow to simulate heating process. Uses 1 "AA" battery, order pkg. above.
49 C 31175—Shpg. wt. 8 oz. . . . . . Kit **$3.49**

Hair Care Accessories

Pretty adornments for any Ideal "growing hair" doll. Includes styling comb, pins, clips, rollers, hairnet, ponytail bands, bows and other decorations.
49 C 35042—Shpg. wt. 3 oz. . . Set **$1.99**

Fashions for Cricket, Velvet and Mia $2.94 each

7 Glad Plaid . . cheery plaid dress with pleated skirt.
49 C 31159—Shpg. wt. 7 oz. **$2.94**

8 Beachnik . . dotted beach robe with belt only. Swimsuit not incl.
49 C 31161—Shpg. wt. 7 oz. **$2.94**

9 Ruffled Up . . frilly pajamas with mod ruffled bottoms.
49 C 31162—Shpg. wt. 7 oz. **$2.94**

10 Smarty Pants . . sporty slacks set.
49 C 31163—Shpg. wt. 7 oz. **$2.94**

NOTE: Dolls, shoes not incl. with outfits above

5-inch Kim with growing hair .. from Uneeda

Kim, case and wardrobe **$3.99**

Give Kim's ponytail a gentle pull and it grows. Give it a tug and it's short again. Jointed vinyl doll wears a pert mini-dress, shoes and panties; comes in a vinyl carry case with 3 extra outfits . . bridal gown, mini-dress and slacks set. Curlers, comb, brush included. Wt. 9 oz.
49 C 35118 . . . . Set **$3.99**

11-inch Valerie with Growin' Pretty Hair $5.99

Pull her ponytail and it grows beautifully long; give it a tug and it's short again. Comb and style her hair . . brush, comb and rollers incl. 11-in. jointed vinyl doll wears a ruffled party dress, shoes and socks.
Shipping wt. 1 lb. 8 oz.
49 C 35069 . . . . **$5.99**

2-doll Case $3.99

Vinyl case with plastic handle and metal clasp. 12x6x20 in. high. Hanger bar and hangers incl. Accessories not incl. Buy it the easy way—order by phone. Shpg. wt. 3 lbs.
79 C 35031C **$3.99**

Accessory Trunk $5.99

Vinyl trunk with shelf, storage bin, hanger bar and hangers. About 7x7x 16 in. high. Plastic handle; clasp. "Passport", tags. Accessories not included. Shpg. wt. 2 lbs.
49 C 35107 . . . . **$5.99**

Clothes Rack $4.99

Molded plastic rack with 2 see-thru vinyl garment bags. About 14x10x18 in. high. Shoes, clothes not included.
49 C 31176—Wt. 2 lbs. 10 oz . . **$4.99**

PCBKM
AEDSLG **Sears** 11

It is curious to note that two grow-hair dolls made by other toy manufacturers are sold on the same page as Ideal's products.

Yesterday's Child™

**Betsy Wetsy and Crissy: © Ideal Toy Corp.

Limited Edition

The names America's children grew up with: Chatty Cathy,* Betsy Wetsy,** and Crissy** are back as works of art made entirely of porcelain. Just 2,000 pieces of each: hand-painted, numbered, and registered. These are tomorrow's heirlooms. Manufactured by Dollspart Porcelain Dolls.

D. Chatty Cathy, Mattel's "talking wonder" of yesterday, had six sayings: all repeated in this full porcelain version with crystal glass eyes. Pony tails, gingham dress, embroidered eyelet jacket, all just as before. 20" tall.
42200-17 . . . . $300.00

E. Betsy Wetsy. Ideal's 1950's baby doll, just as she was, with sparkling crystal glass eyes, striped dress, personalized bib, as a lovely full porcelain treasure. Of course, she drinks and wets. 16".
42200-18 . . . . $300.00

F. Crissy. Who can forget the magic of a doll whose hair could grow? Dollspart recreates the magic, of Ideal's 1969 Crissy in full porcelain, including her orange lace dress. 18" tall.
42200-19 . . . . $300.00

23

Dollspart created the porcelain Crissy, pictured above, and only issued 2,000 of them. She is extremely hard to find.

Crissy's Rooted Hair Really Grows!

Pull her hair and it grows all the way to the floor!
Turn the knob and it's short again!
Style her hair in dozens of fashions!

[1] & [2] **CRISSY THE HAIR-GROW-ING DOLL.** Her silky tresses of soft rooted hair really grow—give every little girl hours of beauty-shop fun! She's a big life-like miss, 17½ in. tall. Body and legs are polyethylene; head and arms are vinyl. She comes dressed in a lacy party dress with matching panties and party shoes. You can order six stunning outfits at right. Shpg. wt. 2.40 lbs.

X 921-7340 A—[1] White Crissy. 8.88
X 921-7399 A—[2] Black Crissy. 8.88

*To get savings when you buy two outfits, state catalog number for each item on same order blank.

2.99 each; any 2 for 5.50*

[3] **CORDUROY JUMPSUIT.** Flare-leg jumpsuit with straps. Long sleeved blouse. Doll not included.
X 921-7514 A—Shipping weight 0.40 lb. 2.99

[4] **QUILTED ROBE SET.** Robe and flare-leg pajamas. Lace trimmed. Doll not included.
X 921-7555 A—Shipping weight 0.40 lb. 2.99

[5] **CAPE OUTFIT.** In plaid. Hooded and plush-trimmed. Doll not included.
X 921-7613 A—Shipping weight 0.40 lb. 2.99

3.99 each; any 2 for 7.50*

[6] **3-PC. BLAZER SET.** Double-breasted blazer, pleated skirt, scarf. Doll not included.
X 921-7621 A—Shipping weight 0.40 lb. 3.99

[7] **AT-HOME OUTFIT.** Flare-leg slacks, blouse, scarf. Doll not included.
X 921-7704 A—Shipping weight 0.40 lb. 3.99

[8] **PARTY DRESS.** Dress of gold-tone metallic fabric. Gold-colored stockings. Doll not included.
X 921-7746 A—Shipping weight 0.40 lb. 3.99

Crissy's Clothes—all in the latest styles!

Toby the Ballerina Doll—Dances to her own music!

[10] **DANCING TOBY.** Turn the key on the back of her head, and music begins to play. Hold the key and she will twirl to the music. She can be positioned. 20-in. high. Arms and head of vinyl. Polyethylene body and legs. Rooted hair. Has flowers on leotard and in hair.
X 922-1680 A—1.50 lbs. 7.99

Thumbelina is an active baby!

[11] **TODDLER THUMBELINA WITH HOBBY HORSE.** Sit little Thumbelina on her rocking horse, pull the string and she rocks back and forth like a real toddler! Toddler Thumbelina is 9-in. tall, vinyl head, arms and legs; rooted hair; painted eyes. She comes fully dressed in her Indian costume with headband.
X 921-7779 A—Shipping weight 1.75 lbs. 5.99

[12] **TODDLER THUMBELINA WITH WALKER.** Thumbelina actually walks in her own "Walker-Trainer". Just pull her string and she "learns" to walk just like a real baby! She's 9-in. tall. Vinyl arms, legs and head; rooted hair; painted eyes. Dressed in her own pink sailor dress and hat.
X 921-7837 A—Shipping weight 2 lbs. 5.99

This page from the 1969 JCPenney's Christmas catalog shows the earliest outfits made by Ideal. Inset photo: 1971 Sears: "Movin' Grovin' Tressy" was sold as "Posin' Tressy."

A & B Crissy With Swirlacurler. She's a fashion doll, 17½ in. tall. Her hair "grows" with a simple tug—retracts easily. You can set and style it with her own plastic Swirlacurler. Just divide her curls, dampen with water, and wrap them around the vertical curler. Comb out when dry and create your own captivating hairstyle for her. Vinyl body, with movable eyes and rooted saran hair. She wears a red and white mini dress. Caution: toy with small parts—see note on page 392.
[A] X 921-3521 A—White Crissy. Mailing weight 1.70 lbs...... **8.88**
[B] X 921-3539 A—Black Crissy. Mailing weight 1.70 lbs...... **8.88**

C & D Velvet With Beauty Braider. She's 15 in. tall. Her hair grows when it's tugged and can be braided. Plastic Beauty Braider has 4 slots—divide her hair into 4 sections, place across the braider openings, and see the beautiful braids you've made. Vinyl body with movable eyes, rooted saran hair. She wears a pretty lavender dress. You'll love playing with her! Caution: toy with small parts—see note on page 392.
[C] X 921-3562 A—White Velvet. Mailing weight 1.70 lbs..... **8.88**
[D] X 921-3653 A—Black Velvet. Mailing weight 1.70 lbs..... **8.88**

E to G Fashion Outfits for Velvet and other 15-in. fashion dolls. Mailing weight each 0.25 lb. Caution: toy with small parts—see note on page 392. Doll and shoes not included.
[E] X 921-9114 A—Maxi coat with hood and fur trim..... Each **2.29**
[F] X 921-9130 A—Red leather-look 3-pc. pants outfit... Each **2.29**
[G] X 921-9213 A—Floral-design granny dress......... Each **2.29**

H to J Fashion Outfits for Velvet and other 15-in. fashion dolls. It's so much fun to dress her in lots of different outfits. Mailing weight each 0.25 lb. Caution: toy with small parts—see note on page 392. Doll and shoes not included.
[H] X 921-9239 A—Green outfit with hat and scarf...... Each **2.29**
[I] X 921-9270 A—Jeans with top, vest and bag........ Each **2.29**
[J] X 921-9288 A—Red peasant dress.................. Each **2.29**
SAVE 60c when you buy any two outfits [E] through [J] together.
List both catalog numbers, pay only........................... **3.98**

Crissy with growing hair and Swirlacurler. Create fashion hairstyles

B Black Crissy with Swirlacurler

D Black Velvet with Beauty Braider

C 8⁸⁸

Velvet has growing hair and a Beauty Braider so you can make braids for her

A 8⁸⁸

E F G **2²⁹** each Any **2** for **3⁹⁸**

H I J K

M 11⁹⁹

Beautiful Baby Crissy has hair that grows! There's a white and a black Baby Crissy

M Bright-Eyed Baby Crissy is the cuddliest Crissy of them all. Her hair really grows. (Make it longer with a simple tug.) Her vinyl body is filled with polyurethane foam, so she's plump, soft and huggable. She wears a 2-pc. romper suit. 24 in. tall. Furniture for 24-in. dolls sold on page 470. Mailing weight 3 lbs.
X 921-3661 A—White Baby Crissy............. **11.99**
X 921-3703 A—Black Baby Crissy............. **11.99**

SAVE THIS CATALOG—order anything on this page till August 24, 1974

Look-Around Crissy and Velvet turn their heads, move at the waist and hold fashion poses when you pull their strings

7⁹⁹ each

L

K Look-Around Crissy is 17½ in. tall. She strikes a fashion pose when you pull her look-around string. Her rooted saran hair grows with a tug. Vinyl body. She wears a green plaid gown. Hair brush and hairstyling booklet included. Caution: toy with small parts—see note on page 392.
X 921-8975 A—Wt. 1.80 lbs...... **7.99**

L Look-Around Velvet is 15 in. tall. Pull her string, and she moves just like Crissy. Her rooted saran hair grows with a tug. Vinyl body. Dressed in a plaid mini dress. Hair brush and hairstyling booklet included. Caution: toy with small parts—see note on page 392.
X 921-8991 A—Wt. 1.40 lbs...... **7.99**

JCPenney **455**

The 1973 JCPenney's catalog shows a small collection of groovy outfits not originally sold through Ideal.

Ready-to-make Sew Simple® Doll Wardrobes..
with pre-cut pieces and step-by-step instructions

Note: Dolls are not included. See Tressy and her friends on pages 9-11; and find Barbie, Ken and friends on pages 13-19.

1
Merrily Mod
$3⁹⁹ each set

2
Wedding Bells
$2⁹⁹ each set

For Barbie and her 11½-inch friends
Snappy Separates $2⁷⁹ set

Informal outfits for fun and action wear. Sew 3 dresses, 2 blouses, skirt, nightie, panties. 3 pairs of shoes, 6 hangers included.
49 C 12424—Wt. 6 oz... Set $2.79

For Tressy, Velvet or any 15 to 17½-inch doll
Fashion Queen $3⁹⁹ set

Join the smart set. Pre-cut pieces for school, town and party dresses, jumper, blouse, bell-bottom slacks, vest. 6 hangers incl.
49 C 1414—Wt. 6 oz.... Set $3.99

Terrific wardrobes to fit 11½-inch Barbie and pals or 6½-inch Dawn and friends

Merrily Mod. The latest fashions. Sew 2 dresses, 2 shirts, 2 blouses, 2 pants outfits, poncho, panties. 3 prs. of shoes, 6 hangers incl.
C 1242–For 11½-in. dolls.
C 12421–For 6½-in. dolls.
Wt. 6 oz...Ea. set $3.99

2 Wedding Bells. Lovely outfits for the big day. Sew bridal gown, veil, bridesmaid gown, stole, formal gown, panties. 3 prs. of shoes, 6 hangers included.
49 C 12425—For 11½-in. dolls.
49 C 12426—For 6½-in. dolls.
Wt. set 6 oz.... Ea. set $2.99

For Skipper, Fluff and their 9-inch friends
Pre-teen Scene $2⁷⁹ set

Even junior misses want to be fashionable—let them join the trendy pre-teen scene. Sew 4 dresses, skirt, blouse, pajamas, panties. 3 pairs of shoes, 6 hangers included.
Shipping weight 6 ounces.
49 C 12423............Set $2.79

For Ken, Brad or any 12-inch fella
Groovy Threads $2⁹⁹ set

For the dapper look for that lucky guy. Sew 2 shirts, slacks, jacket and pajamas. For formal wear—tuxedo jacket and trousers, cummerbund, bow tie. Shoes, 6 hangers included.
Shipping weight 6 ounces.
49 C 12427..............Set $2.99

BETSY ROSS NEEDLECRAFT KITS

3
Beginning Cross-Stitch

$2⁷⁹ each set

Beginning Needlepoint

3 Serves as an introduction to cross-stitch embroidery. Set

4 Go creative—needlepoint's fun

4

Ready-to-make outfits for the girls were sold along with other size outfits for other dolls on this page from the 1971 Sears Wish Book. Tressy is modeling one outfit proudly! Barbie, Ken, Brad, Skipper, and Fluff are trademarks of Mattel, Inc.

Sew a Doll Wardrobe..it's easy and fun!
Pieces are pre-cut, ready-to-sew..step-by-step instructions are included

Priced to be **SOMETHING SPECIAL**
Mix 'n Match
Was $2.69
$2⁵⁷ set

Priced to be **SOMETHING SPECIAL**
Trousseau
Was $2.99
$2⁷⁶ set

For all 11½-inch fashion dolls.. Barbie, Jamie, Julia and friends

London Look $3⁹⁹ set

Sun Valley $3⁹⁹ set

NEW! Teen Wardrobe
For Crissy, Tressy and all other 17½-inch dolls $3⁹⁹ without doll

CUT 4%. Mix 'n Match Set. Make a dress, 2 blouses, jumper, skirt, suitdress with jacket and flannel nightie. Belt, purse, hangers, shoes and accessories included. Wt. 6 oz.
49 N 1493.........Set **$2.57**

CUT 7%. Bride's Trousseau Set. Sew bridal gown, veil, bridesmaid gown, stole, formal and jacket. Gloves, shoes, hangers incl. Wt. 6 oz.
49 N 1457....Set **$2.76**

Sun Valley Set. Sew beautiful outfits for tennis, swimming, skiing, cheerleading, skating and ballet. Sports equipment incl. Shpg. wt. 6 oz.
49 N 1458.....Set $3.99

London Look Set. The latest fashions. Sew 3 dresses, pantsuit, jacket, slacks set, coat, kerchief, pajamas, hat. Purse, boots, hangers. Wt. 6 oz.
49 N 1456.....Set $3.99

Pre-cut pieces for school, town and party dresses; jumper, blouse, bell-bottom slacks, vest. Hangers included. Wt. 6 oz.
49 N 1414.........Set $3.99

NOTE: DOLLS NOT INCLUDED WITH WARDROBES

Create beautiful towels with Embroidery and Applique Set
$2⁹⁹

Set includes 8 towels—4 printed and ready to be embroidered, 4 to be appliqued with colorful designs from Japan—plus embroidery hoop, 2 needles, 2 skeins of thread, instructions.
49 N 12032—Shpg. wt. 1 lb. Set $2.99

Fully-lined Sewing Basket and Accessories
$2⁹⁹

Hand-woven basket keeps all your accessories organized and easy to find. Spool tray holds needles, threader, tape measure, thimble, blunt scissors, 4 spools of thread, ABC of Sewing book. 8½x7x4 in. Taiwan.
49 N 1222—Shpg. wt. 1 lb. 4 oz. $2.99

Plush Animals to sew by hand or machine
$2⁹⁹ each

Each kit includes pre-cut acrylic pile pieces with plastic eyes riveted in, complete instructions. Finished animals are hand washable.
Panda Kit—makes a real pajama bag. Includes 2 pompons, braid trim, loop for hanging. 14 in. tall.
49 N 14035—Shipping wt. 8 oz. ......Kit $2.99
Dog Kit. 9 in. tall pooch sits up, ears pose. Incl. wiring, plastic foam stuffing, pompon, ribbon.
49 N 14034—Shipping wt. 8 oz. ......Kit $2.99

PCBKM
AEDSLG Sears **565**

Mom could sew an entire wardrobe designed to fit Crissy and Tressy with the set shown on this page. Notice that the picture shows a number one Crissy from the previous year, though not offered in this Sears 1970 catalog.

112

THEIR HAIR GROWS
Press each girl's tummy, then pull her rooted hair to make it "grow".. a knob on her back winds it short again

1

2

3 4 5 6 7

Mod Fashions for Crissy and Tressy

17½-inch Tressy $8.87

17½-inch Crissy $8.87

15-in. $8.87 Velvet

Introducing Velvet. Crissy's *younger cousin.* She's 15 inches tall .. looks so sweet, perky and almost real. With big violet eyes, silky rooted hair that grows to her knees, smooth vinyl skin. Jointed. Wt. 1 lb. 4 oz.
49 N 35028....$8.87

Outfits for Velvet

1 Lace-trimmed pajamas, peignoir. Shoes. Wt. 4 oz.
49 N 32551....$2.97

2 Mini-coat, cloche hat with pompon. Shoes. Wt. 4 oz.
49 N 32549....$2.97

Crissy's back again. Looking as spectacular as ever with her deep dark eyes and flowing auburn hair that's such fun to style. Vinyl; jointed; 17½ inches tall.
49 N 35041—Shpg. wt. 1 lb. 6 oz................$8.87

Isn't Tressy a beauty? She's a glorious brunette with hair you'll love to style, vinyl flesh-look skin and large go-to-sleep eyes. Jointed; 17½ in. tall. With her own hair-styling accessories. Headband not incl.
49 N 35029—Shpg. wt. 1 lb. 6 oz................$8.87

Outfits for Crissy and Tressy

3 Satin mini-dress, matching fringed scarf. Shoes.
49 N 32555—Shipping weight 4 oz. $2.97

4 Lace-trimmed bell-bottom pants, robe. Sandals.
49 N 30752—Shipping weight 5 oz. $2.97

5 Bell-bottoms, shirt, poncho. Peace medal, sandals.
49 N 32554—Shipping weight 4 oz. $2.97

6 Sparkly gold-color mini-dress, stockings, shoes.
49 N 32552—Shipping weight 4 oz. $2.97

7 Hooded cape with fur-look trim, pompons. Shoes.
49 N 30751—Shipping weight 5 oz. $2.97

NOTE: Dolls not included with outfits 1 through 7

Hair Care Kit. Styling brush, rollers, clips, pins, net, ponytail bands, bows, other decorations.
Shpg. wt. 3 oz.
49 N 35042 ....$1.99

2-Doll Trunk. Vinyl. Hanger bar, hangers. Molded handle, metal clasp. 12x6½x20½-in. Dolls, accessories not included. Shpg. wt. 3 lbs.
79 N 35031C $3.99

THUMBELINA
..only 9 inches tall.. just pull her string to make her move

8 Rocks in her cradle

11 Sits up, throws a kiss

12 Toddles in her walker

14 Bells on her toes jingle as she walks with you

15 Rides her hobby horse

9

10 Drives her car forward or backward

13

16

Soft cloth-bodied babies with vinyl heads and rooted hair you can comb

8 **Newborn Thumbelina.** Irresistible squirmer.
49N30756—No crib. Wt. 1 lb. 2 oz. $5.44

9 **Rocking Crib.** All plastic. 10x5x8 inches high.
49 N 30757—Shipping weight 12 oz.....$1.49

10 **Speedy Thumbelina with Car.** Wind string and off she goes. Plastic car 9⅞x4x3⅞ inches.
49 N 35043—Shpg. wt. 1 lb. 8 oz..... Set $6.44

11 **Kissin' Thumbelina with Carriage.** In or out of carriage, she sits up, opens big blue eyes, throws a kiss. Plastic carriage. 14x5¼x10⅞ in.

12 **Toddler Thumbelina the Sailor Girl.**
49 N 30754—No walker. Wt. 1 lb. $5.44

13 **Walker.** All plastic. 7x6x6 inches high.
49 N 30769—Shipping weight 12 oz. ...$1.49

14 **Jingle Thumbelina.** Pull string, hold her hands and she'll walk with you. Bells on her toes.
49 N 35044—Shipping weight 1 lb. 2 oz. $5.44

15 **Toddler Thumbelina the Indian Princess.**
49 N 30768—No horse. Wt. 1 lb. $5.44

16 **Rocking Horse.** All plastic. 8x8x3 inches high.

The Sears 1970 catalog offers Tressy in her first-issue outfit, though the headband was not included. Velvet was introduced, and Crissy was back in her second-issue outfit, the satin aqua minidress.

The Wedding Belles

Movin' Groovin' Tressy and Cricket with twist-turn swivel waists .. dressed for a special occasion in glamorous Bride and Bridesmaid Gift Sets

(1 and 2) Every day's a very special wedding day for these dolls. Dress them up, pose them and style their growing hair any way you wish. Swing their shoulders around—their bouncy curls toss from side to side. Vinyl.

1 Cricket Gift Set with lacy gown, mini-veil and bouquet. 15-inch doll comes dressed in a bright mini dress. Wt. 1 lb. 6 oz.
49 N 35133......Set $9.79
Bridesmaid outfit only, fits any 15-inch doll.
49 N 35135—Wt. 7 oz..$2.08

2 Tressy Gift Set with elegant gown, veil and bouquet. 17½-in. doll is dressed in a satin mini dress for rehearsal. Wt. 1 lb. 6 oz.
49 N 35132......Set $9.88
Bridal outfit only, fits any 17½-inch doll. Wt. 7 oz.
49 N 35134.........$2.08

HAIR CARE ACCESSORIES FOR ANY GROWING HAIR DOLL

Hair Setting Kit $3.49 without battery
Incl. "curler warmer" with rollers, "hair spray", comb, brush, "mirror" and hair decorations plus a handy styling booklet. Plastic "warmer" lights-up curlers to simulate heating process. Uses 1 "AA" battery, order pkg. below. Ages 5 to 10.
49 N 31175—Wt. 8 oz....Kit $3.49
"AA" Batteries. Package of 6.
49 N 8402—Wt. 6 oz......Pkg. 99c

Doll's Hair Accessories include styling comb, pins, clips, rollers, hairnet, bows and other decorations.
49 N 35042—Wt. 3 oz.....Set $1.99

3 Crissy Way-out Wig Set incl. a curly layered wig, wig block and brush. Doll (shown below, at right) not incl.
49 N 35127—Wt. 8 oz....Set $2.41

NOTE for all items on page: Not recommended for ages 3 and under.

$2.41
3

Movin' Groovin' Cricket Gift Set
1 $9.79

Movin' Groovin' Tressy Gift Set
$9.88 **2**

424 Sears

The year 1972 saw the release of these glorious sets, the Cricket Bridesmaid Gift Set and the Tressy Bride Gift Set. Note, too, that the bridal outfits were also sold separately in this Sears catalog.

114

FASHIONS FOR 15-INCH DOLLS
including Velvet, Cricket and Dina

All 3 outfits in 1 set

Dolls, shoes not included **$4.75** set

Go Mix and Match . . a whole great wardrobe set including a match-up jumper, blouse, overalls, polo shirt and hat *plus* a bright mini dress.
49 N 35137—Wt. 8 oz. . . . . . Set $4.75

High Fashion Outfits
For 15-in. dolls (not incl.)

3 Blazering; skirt, blazer, dickey.
49 N 35146—Wt. 8 oz. $3.66

4 On the Lamb: wet-look coat, hat.
49 N 35145—Wt. 8 oz. $3.66

5 Dandy Denims; slacks, top, headband. Shipping weight 7 oz.
49 N 32611 . . . . $2.94

6 Frontier Gear; midi coat and purse.
49 N 32612—Wt. 7 oz. $2.94

NOTE: Shoes not included with outfits (3 thru 10)

Shoe Wardrobe $1.95

For 15-inch dolls. Incl. 2 pairs of shoes, 2 pair of long boots. Ages 5 to 10. Shpg. wt. 7 oz.
49 N 31164 . . $1.95

FASHIONS FOR 17½-INCH DOLLS
including Crissy, Tressy, Brandi

All 3 outfits in 1 set

Dolls, shoes not included **$4.75** set

Weekender Set . . a perfect travel wardrobe including sailor outfit with slacks, blouse, scarf *plus* shorty nightgown and robe for sweet dreaming.
49 N 35136—Wt. 8 oz. . . . . . Set $4.75

Designer Originals
for 17½-in. dolls (not incl.)

7 Blazering; maxi-skirt, blazer, dickey. Buy it the easy way—order by phone.
49 N 35144—Wt. 8 oz. $3.66

8 Very Vanilla; maxi-coat, cloche hat. Shipping weight 8 ounces.
49 N 35147 . . . . $3.66

9 Funky Feathers; jeans, top, necklace. Shipping weight 7 ounces.
49 N 32587 . . . . $2.94

10 Star Shine: mod midi-coat, scarf.
49 N 32588—Wt. 7 oz. $2.94

Shoe Wardrobe $1.95

For 17½-inch dolls. Incl. 3 pairs of shoes, 1 pair of long boots. Ages 5 to 10. Shpg. wt. 8 oz.
49 N 31165 . . $1.95

Velvet and Crissy
Each doll turns her head and moves her waist when you pull her look-around string. Hold the string and she'll hold the pose

Look-Around Velvet $7.67 | **Look-Around Crissy** $7.99

(11 and 12) They're so graceful and lifelike! Each turns her head, then her body, to look from side to side . . . you control the movement. Or choose a pose and they'll hold it. Vinyl dolls have stylable growing hair.

11 Look-Around Velvet in a print mini. 15 in. tall. Wt. 1 lb. 4 oz.
49 N 3511 . . . . $7.67

12 Look-Around Crissy in a long gown. 17½ in. tall. Wt. 1 lb. 8 oz.
49 N 3509 . . . . $7.99

Note for all items on page: Items not recommended for children ages 3 and under.

2-Doll Case has hangers, hanger bar incl. Accessories not incl. Vinyl case is 12x6x20 inches high. Ages 5 to 10. Shpg. wt. 3 lbs.
79N35031C . . $3.99

Accessory Trunk with shelf, storage bin, hanger bar, hangers, "passport" tags. Vinyl; 7x7x16 in. high. Accessories not incl. Ages 5 to 10. Wt. 2 lbs.
49 N 35107 . . . . $5.95

PBCOM KDGAE [Sears] 425

This 1972 Sears page also had beautiful clothing for Crissy, Velvet, and their friends. These outfits were available only through Sears.

Little 6-inch Lella with 3 extra outfits including a bridal gown

$8⁹⁹ set

This mini-sized doll comes with her own wedding gown and trousseau. Set includes gown and veil, coat, country-style dress, scarf and a polka dot party dress. Shoes.

Little Lella has shiny rooted hair, go-to-sleep eyes, vinyl skin. Jointed. Italy. Shipping wt. 8 oz.
49N37148—Set $8.99

NOTE FOR ALL ITEMS ON PAGE: NOT recommended for children 3 years old and under

How should Corinne wear her hair? Any way you want!

15-inch Corinne from Italo Cremona dresses for nearly every occasion in 6 high-fashion outfits

Corinne plus outfit
$7⁹⁹ each

Outfit only
$4⁴⁷ each

(1 thru 6) Change Corinne's hairstyle as often as you change her outfit. Each of these Italian beauties has easy-to-style rooted hair, go-to-sleep eyes, sunglasses and comb. Jointed vinyl and polyethylene. Ages 5 to 10. (Outfits only: Wt. 10 oz. each).

1 Corinne in knit top, tights, skirt, hat.
49N32072–Wt.1 lb.8oz.$7.99
49N3258–Outfit only . 4.47

2 Pretty Corinne looks so stylish in her knit top, tights, pant skirt and vest.
49N3204–Wt.1 lb.8 oz. $7.99
49N32557–Outfit only 4.47

3 Corinne in long country-style gown. Buy it the easy way—order by phone.
49N3207–Wt.1 lb. 8 oz. $7.99
49N3256–Outfit only . 4.47

4 Corinne dresses up in her elegant maxi-coat and hat.
49N32073–Wt.1 lb.8 oz. $7.99
49N32582–Outfit only 4.47

5 Corinne in mod slacks set and vest.
49N32071–Wt.1 lb.8oz.$7.99
49N3257–Outfit only . 4.47

6 Corinne looks super in her bright blouse, mini-skirt, boots and cap.
49N32074–Wt.1 lb.8oz.$7.99
49N32583–Outfit only 4.47

Dolls with Growing Hair

Just press doll's tummy. pull her hair and it grows. A knob on her back winds it short.

(7 thru 9) Change their hairdos from a short bob to luxuriously long. Pose them . . they're all jointed vinyl. For ages 5 to 10.

7 15-inch Dina with twist-turn swivel waist and sun-kissed blonde hair. Wears a sporty overall sun suit and tie-up clogs.
49N35046–Wt. 1 lb. 6 oz. .$5.53

8 17½-inch Brandi with twist-turn swivel waist, sun-kissed blonde hair and a lovely tan. She's dressed in a high-fashion swimsuit and tie-up clogs.
49N35045–Wt. 1 lb. 8 oz. .$5.99

9 17½-inch Tressy wears a fabulous mini dress. She has bright brown eyes, pretty black hair and a sweet smile.
49N35122–Wt. 1 lb. 6 oz. .$7.97

7 15-inch Dina
$5⁵³

9 17½-inch Tressy
$7⁹⁷

8 17½-inch Brandi
$5⁹⁹

IDEAL

"That sounds like fun"

17½-inch Talky Crissy with growing hair . . says 6 phrases

$12⁹⁹

Ask her a question, pull her ring, 17½-in. Crissy *may* say "Why not?" *or* she may say "I don't think so." Press her tummy, pull her hair—it grows 'n grows. Wears a long, elegant robe. Jointed vinyl. For ages 5 to 10. Shpg. wt. 1 lb. 12 oz.
49 N 35131 ..$12.99

Note: See more growing hair dolls on next page.

PBLCOS MKDGAE **Sears** **423**

Talky Crissy is offered at a significantly higher price than her friends in the 1972 Sears catalog. Black Tressy is available in the original Tressy issue outfit. This doll was not a Posin' or Movin' Groovin' model.

The World of Crissy

BEAUTIFUL CRISSY
the famous doll with hair that "grows"

Only **5⁷⁷** *when you buy her 5-outfit wardrobe, too!*
Crissy **6⁶⁶** *separately*

③ Crissy is an exquisite beauty with delicately tinted features, lifelike vinyl head and arms, lovely deep-set open-and-close eyes. Her luxurious rooted hair can be combed and styled, made to "grow" from short to long. She can stand alone or be posed gracefully. Wears mini dress, panties, high-style shoes. Abt. 17½ in. tall.
48 T 10200—Crissy doll only. Ship. wt. 1 lb. 6 oz........6.66

FABULOUS VALUE. Crissy is only 5.77 when you buy her in combination with stylish outfits, (4) below!
48 T 10224—Crissy plus Outfits. Ship. wt. 1 lb. 13 oz...11.76

FABULOUS VALUE

Your choice **7⁹⁶**

Crissy with Swirlacurler Velvet with Beauty Braider

①② FABULOUS VALUES at Wards! Glamorous "growing-hair" dolls seen on TV, now more fun than ever. They come with special hair arrangers; you can set Crissy's hair in captivating curls, Velvet's in bewitching braids—real crowning glories! Dolls have lifelike vinyl heads and arms, open-and-close eyes, posable jointed bodies, rooted hair that grows. For more play fun, buy them extra outfits at right.
(1) Crissy with Swirlacurler and hair-style booklet. Wears smart plaid jumper with blouse, slippers. About 17½ in. tall.
48 T 10225—Black Doll   48 T 10227—White Doll
Ship. wt. 1 lb. 11 oz...........................each 7.96
(2) Velvet with Beauty Braider. Pretty print dress, slippers.
48 T 10228—Abt. 15 in. tall. Ship. wt. 1 lb. 11 oz.........7.96

5 Outfits for 17½-18-in. Dolls 5⁹⁹ set
④ Smart wardrobe for Crissy, or other fashion dolls. Clothes for all occasions: bright pants with long blouse, shift 'n shorts, stylish long skirt with blouse, lace-trimmed pj's, "fur" edged shift. *Dolls not included.*
48 T 11036—Ship. wt. 7 oz.:....................set 5.99

Cinnamon with Hairdoodler 4⁴⁴

⑤ Pull butterfly string—Hairdoodler styles little sister Cinnamon's hair! Posable vinyl body. Wears 2-pc. playsuit, slippers.
48 T 10229—13½ in. tall. Ship. wt. 12 oz. 4.44

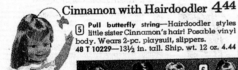

4 Outfits for Cinnamon 3⁹⁹

⑥ Up-to-the-minute styles. You can change her clothes when you change her "hair-do." For all occasions: long tunic with swingy "palazzo pants," frilly pajamas and a robe with belt, dotted daytime dress. *Dolls not included.*
48 T 11044—Ship. wt. 12 oz........................set 3.99

5 Outfits for 15-in. Dolls 4⁸⁷ set
⑦ Stylish outfits for Velvet, or other fashion dolls. Clothes for all occasions: long tunic with swingy pants, print dress with apron, colorful jump suit, body shirt with long split skirt, frilly pj's. *Dolls not included.*
48 T 11037—Ship. wt. 7 oz....................set 4.87

Boots 'n Shoes 1⁷⁷ set
⑧ Shoe fashions for Crissy. Boots, clogs, slippers in assorted colors. Wt. 8 oz.
48 T 11014..........set 1.77

Shoe fashions for Velvet. An assortment of colorful boots, clogs, slippers. Wt. 8 oz.
48 T 11015..........set 1.77

New! Crissy Beauty Parlor 7⁸⁸
⑨ A fabulous "salon" for glamour dolls. You've seen it on TV. Special chair where Crissy, Velvet or other growing-hair fashion dolls can sit while you style their hair. Set contains Swirlacurler, Beauty Braider, Hairdoodler, special comb and brush, styling booklet, an assortment of ribbons, ties and hair-do accessories. Antiqued-finish plastic. About 12x6x8 in. high.
48 T 11642—Ship. wt. 1 lb. 5 oz....................7.88

Tote Case for Fashion Dolls 4⁹⁹
⑩ Take Crissy or her friends along with you. White "wet-look" vinyl covered case about 11x5x22 in. high has molded handle, clasp closing. Space for doll and outfits. *Doll and clothing are not included.*
48 T 11624 X—Ship. wt. 3 lbs. 3 oz....................4.99
SAVE THIS CATALOG—You can order toys until Aug. 31, 1974

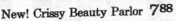

The 1973 Wards catalog sold quite a few non-Ideal-made outfits for the grow-hair family, including Cinnamon!

2 12⁷⁷
Talky Crissy speaks 12 phrases

1 MOVIN' GROOVIN' CRISSY has hair that grows to knee-length. Brush, hair styling booklet. Her waist twists and turns to any position. Plastic body, rooted hair, moving eyes. Wears midi outfit, boots. 17½ in. tall.
X 922-3702 A—Wt. 2 lbs.................. 9.77

2 TALKY CRISSY says 12 different phrases. Rooted hair grows and grows, has everything you need to set it: rollers, ribbons, yarn ties, rubber bands, bobby pins, brush, and endpapers. Plastic body with moving eyes, pretty hostess dress. 17½ in. tall.
X 922-3595 A—Wt. 2 lbs.................. 12.77

3 PRETTY BLONDE KERRY fits all of Crissy's clothes. Rooted hair "grows" to knee-length. Moving eyes, plastic body. 17½ in. tall.
X 922-3603 A—Wt. 1.50 lbs................. 6.77

4 BEAUTIFUL CRISSY has hair that will grow to knee-length. Style brush included. Body and legs are polyethylene, head and arms are vinyl. Party dress, panties and shoes. 17½ in. tall.
X 921-7159 A—Wt. 2.40 lbs................. 6.77

6 6⁷⁷
Kerry, Crissy's friend

3

4
6.77

Clothes fit 17½ in. fashion dolls

5 SHORTS WITH MAXI COAT-VEST. Red shorts, navy blue coat. White shirt.
X 922-3611 A†—Wt. 0.40 lb. Ea. 1.99; any 3 for 5.00

6 RUFFLED DRESS. Ribbon belt.
X 922-3629 A†-0.40 lb. Ea. 1.99; any 3 for 5.00

7 PURPLE PANTSUIT with bag, headband.
X 922-3637 A†-0.40 lb. Ea. 1.99; any 3 for 5.00

8 2-PC. PEPLUM SUIT has blue skirt, white jacket.
X 922-3645 A†-0.40 lb. Ea. 3.49; any 2 for 6.00

9 BEACH OUTFIT. Swimsuit, coat.
X 922-3652 A†-0.40 lb. Ea. 3.49; any 2 for 6.00
*State catalog number for each item when you order

5 **6** **7** 3⁴⁹ each
any **2** for 6⁰⁰*
[8] or [9] **8** **9**

1 9⁷⁷
New Movin' Groovin' Crissy

1⁹⁹ each
any **3** for 5⁰⁰*
[5], [6], or [7]

10 3⁸⁸

10 HAIR STYLING SET. Brush, comb, curler warmer set, 1 can of "pretend" hair spray, curlers, make-up mirror, style book, tray. Uses 1 AA battery (not included— order below item [11]).
X 922-3678 A—Wt. 2.50 lbs.................. 3.88

11 HAIR DRYER—actually blows air to dry hair. Plastic. Operates on 2 AA batteries (not incl.—order below).
X 922-3660 A—Wt. 1.50 lbs.................. 3.19
AA Batteries. Sold in package of 4, Wt. 0.40 lb.
X 957-1902 A..............Order 1 package for 69c

12 & **13** WORLD OF LOVE DOLLS are plastic with hand painted coloring, rooted hair. Bend at neck, shoulders, hips, knees. In pants outfit.
X 922-3785 A—[12] Blonde. 1 lb. 9¼ in. tall.... 3.44
X 922-3793 A—[13] Brunette. 1 lb. 9¼ in. tall.... 3.44

14 RED JUMPSUIT with embroidered ribbon snap belt, white hat. Blue felt fringed shoulder bag. Fits [12], [13].
X 922-3801 A†—Wt. 0.40 lb. 1.99 each; any 3 for 5.00

15 MULTICOLOR QUILTED PANTS, black top. Chain belt. Fits [12] and [13].
X 922-3819 A†—Wt. 0.40 lb. 1.99 each; any 3 for 5.00

16 MINI DRESS with set-in belt in blue and yellow. Yellow mesh knee socks. Fits [12] and [13].
X 922-3827 A†—Wt. 0.40 lb. 1.99 each; any 3 for 5.00

12 3⁴⁴ each **13**

1⁹⁹ each
any **3** for 5⁰⁰*
[14], [15], or [16]

16

11 3¹⁹

14 **15**

1 MOVIN' GROOVIN' VELVET is Crissy's cousin— has rooted blonde hair that grows from a neat bob to knee-length. Twists and turns from the waist. Rooted hair, moving eyes, plastic body. With brush and hair styling booklet. Wears a cute mini dress. 15 in. tall.
X 922-3835 A—Wt. 1.50 lbs.............. 9.77

2 TALKY VELVET with luxurious hair that grows and grows, and comes with rollers, ribbons, yarn ties, rubber bands, bobby pins, brush and end papers. Speaks 6 different phrases. Rooted hair, moving eyes, plastic body. She wears a quilted hostess dress with ruffled bib front. Stands 15 in. tall.
X 922-3710 A—Wt. 1.50 lbs.............. 12.77

3 MIA. Moving eyes, long rooted brown hair that grows. Plastic body stands 15 in. tall.
X 922-3728 A—Wt. 1.50 lbs.............. 6.77

4 VELVET has blonde rooted locks that go down to her knees. Moving eyes. Plastic body stands 15 in. tall.
X 921-7258 A—Wt. 1.25 lbs.............. 6.77

Clothes for 15 in. dolls Dolls not included.

5 SUEDED COTTON MINI VEST-COAT in brown with orange jumper. Fringe belt on vest-coat.
X 922-3736 A—Wt. 0.40 lb...1.99 each; any 3 for 5.00

6 PRETTY PEASANT DRESS is in shades of purple with red turtleneck shirt. Purple vest, white trim.
X 922-3744 A—Wt. 0.40 lb...1.99 each; any 3 for 5.00

7 GREEN PANTS with multi-striped, long-sleeved shirt. Plastic and metal-chain belt.
X 922-3751 A—Wt. 0.40 lb...1.99 each; any 3 for 5.00

8 ORANGE POLKA DOT OUTFIT with matching head scarf. Charming posy pattern. One-piece suit.
X 922-3769 A—Wt. 0.40 lb...3.49 each; any 2 for 6.00

9 ONE-PIECE PAJAMA OUTFIT with ruffled cuffs, smart white bib. Pale blue.
X 922-3777 A—Wt. 0.40 lb...3.49 each; any 2 for 6.00

3 6⁷⁷ Mia is Velvet's new friend

2 12⁷⁷ Talky Velvet says 6 phrases clearly

7 1⁹⁹ each any 3 for 5⁰⁰* [5], [6], or [7]

3⁴⁹ each 2 for 6⁰⁰*

1 9⁷⁷ New Movin' Groovin' Velvet poses any way you want

12 4.44

13 4.88

10 FABULOUS DOLLIKIN®. She sits, bends, does exercises. Jointed at ankles, knees, hips, waist, shoulders, wrists, and elbows. Long rooted hair. Plastic. Wears bell-bottom jumpsuit. Stands 11½ in. tall.
X 921-2481 A—Wt. 0.60 lb................. 1.44

11 EVENING OUTFIT, SLACK OUTFIT, COAT AND HAT SET. Elegant evening pants topped by jacket. Slacks, jacket, boots, bag, and glasses. Coat, hat, boots, bag, scarf, record player and sandals. Dolls shown are not included. For Dollikin® and all other 11½ in. fashion dolls.
X 921-2416 A—Wt. 0.50 lb......Order 1 set for 2.88

12 SPACIOUS VINYL TOTE BAG with a quilted vinyl interior—plenty of space for Crissy and her outfits (doll and outfits not included). Molded plastic carrying handle. 20 in. high.
X 922-3694 A—Mail. wt. 1.50 lbs................. 4.44

13 CLOTHES RACK WITH 2 GARMENT BAGS. Painted plastic rack with 2 vinyl bags. Will hold outfits, accessories for Crissy, Velvet, Kerry, and Mia. 18 in. high.
X 922-3686 A—Mail. wt. 3 lbs................. 4.88

11 2⁸⁸ set of 3 outfits

10 1⁴⁴

SAVE THIS CATALOG—order anything on these two pages until August 26, 1972

*State catalog number for each item when you order

JCPenney 465

Both Pages: The 1972 JCPenney's catalog had a very nice selection of grow-hair girls available, including some of the most well made and attractive catalog clothing ever made for them. (1972 JCPenney's pages are courtesy of Diane Wall)

17½-in.
Crissy
with Twirly
Beads
$9⁸⁸

[11]

[12]
15-in. Velvet
with Swirly
Daisies
$9⁸⁸

[13]
12-in. Cinnamon
with Curly
Ribbons
$5⁹⁴

Dolls with hair design ornaments

(11 thru 13) Dolls made of vinyl. They have hair ornaments to style their hair that grows. You can design attractive hair styles quick as a wink. Go-to-sleep eyes. Movable arms and legs.

11 17½-inch Crissy with Twirly Beads. Just turn the knob in her back to make her hair long or short. Long country-style dress. For ages 4 to 10. Wt. 1 lb. 10 oz.
49 N 32089 . . . .$9.88

12 15-inch Velvet with Swirly Daisies. Just turn the knob in her back to make her hair long or short. Dressed in a sprightly mini-dress. For ages 3 to 8. Wt. 1 lb. 10 oz.
49 N 32091 . . . .$9.88

13 12-inch Cinnamon with Curly Ribbons. Poseable doll has hair that grows. Denim jumper, shirt. For children ages 3 to 8. Shpg. wt. 12 oz.
49 N 32092 . . . .$5.94

NOTE: Items on this page (except dressing table, walker-stroller) not recommended for children under 3 years of age due to small parts.

Give your baby doll
some quick fashion changes.
Just look at these sets
in different size ranges . .

"BABY" CLOTHES

9-pc. Knit Wardrobe Sets
For dolls 10 to 21 inches tall
$5⁹⁹ sets for 10 to 15-in. dolls

You'll have a hard time deciding which outfit to dress your babe in . . they're all so pretty. Each is machine knit . . and feels so soft. Wardrobe set includes a 2-piece slacks set, dress and pants, jumper with body suit and three hangers.

To order the easiest way, look in your phone book white pages under "Sears, Roebuck and Co., Catalog Sales" for number to call.

For doll heights	Catalog Number	Shpg. wt.		Price
		lbs.	oz.	
10 to 12 in.	49 N 32541	. . . .	12	$5.99
13 to 15 in.	49 N 32542	1	. . . .	5.99
16 to 18 in.	49 N 32543	1	4	6.99
19 to 21 in.	49 N 32544	1	8	6.99

18-pc. Cotton Wardrobe Sets
For dolls 10 to 22 inches tall $3⁹⁹ sets for 10 to 15-in. dolls

An outfit for any occasion . . each set includes 2-piece playwear ensemble, 2 dress and pants sets, sleeveless dress and a 3-piece pram suit including sacque, bonnet and pants. Set also includes 5 hangers, 2 bottles and a comb.

For doll heights	Catalog Number	Wt. oz.	Price
10 to 11 in.	49 N 32531	6	$3.99
12 to 13 in.	49 N 32532	6	3.99
14 to 15 in.	49 N 32533	6	3.99
16 to 17 in.	49 N 32534	7	4.99
18 to 19 in.	49 N 32535	7	4.99
20 to 22 in.	49 N 32536	8	4.99

Non-folding Dressing Table
$7⁴⁷

Now you can dress and change your "baby" on her own dressing table. Wicker-look fiber stand has wood frame and vinyl top. 18½x9x18¼ in. high. Holds dolls to 16 in. tall. Ages 3 to 10. Wt. 7 lbs.
79 N 33516C $7.47

Walker-Stroller
$3⁹⁴

Take your doll for a walk on a sunny afternoon. Metal walker is 15x9x19 in. high. Plastic wheels, metal tray. Colorful wooden beads. Detachable handle for transport. Seats dolls to 18 in. tall. Partly assembled. Ages 2 to 5. Shpg. wt. 2 lbs. 6 oz.
49 N 33061 . . . .$3.94

PBC 063 **Sears** 439

The 1974 grow-hair girls were only given a small amount of space in this 1974 Sears catalog.

She's life size! Baby Crissy
with growing hair

Save 2.48

12⁹⁶

Only **12⁹⁶** when you buy her 4-outfit layette, too!

Doll separately **15⁴⁴**

Baby Crissy is adorable, a cuddly, lifelike baby 24 in. tall. You've seen her on TV. She's soft, huggable and lightweight, her jointed vinyl body is filled with plastic foam. Petal-soft baby skin feels real. Pretty auburn hair "grows" from short to long with just a tug of her hair-string. Baby Crissy is dressed in dainty pink infant-style dress with matching panties.

Special layette designed to fit Baby Crissy, other 23-24 in. baby dolls, includes a change of clothes for every time of day—bright red jumper-dress with dotted sleeves and yoke, soft flannel 'jamies, 2-pc. playsuit with long pants, and sunsuit with matching panties. It's a layette to delight Baby Crissy's new Mommy!

48 G 10121—Doll only. Ship. wt. 4 lbs. 8 oz...15.44
48 G 11066—Layette only. Ship. wt. 1 lb......6.99

Save 2.48 on special combination. Baby Crissy is only 12.96 when you buy layette, too. Wt. 5 lbs. 8 oz.
48 G 10123—Baby Crissy and Layette.......19.95

Tote Case for Fashion Dolls

4⁹⁹

Smart carrying case for Tiffany, Jennifer, Crissy or Velvet. Take them along wherever you go. Shiny "wet-look" vinyl with colorful decoration, says "Swingin' Set" on the front. With handle, metal clasp. Room for doll and wardrobe. Abt. 11x5x 22 in. high. *Clothing, doll not incl.* Wt. 3 lbs. 3 oz.
48 G 11624..........4.99

SAVE THIS CATALOG
Toys available 'til
August 31, 1975

The World of Crissy

Beautiful Dolls with hair that "grows"
Crissy with Twirly Beads
Velvet with Swirly Daisies

Your choice only **7⁸⁹** when you buy their 4-outfit wardrobe, too!

Dolls separately **9⁴⁴** each

7, 8 **Crissy and Velvet are exquisite beauties** with lifelike vinyl heads, delicately tinted features, lovel deep-set sleeping eyes. Their luxurious rooted hair can be combed and styled, made to "grow" fron short to long. Jointed bodies—they can stand alone or be posed. Not recommended for children under 3

7 **Crissy with Twirly Beads.** She's gone country-style in a pretty gingham check with ruffles. Wears long twirly beads in her modish hair-do. The beads twirl and twist Crissy's hair into dozens of styles. Abt. 17¼ in. tall. Wt. 1 lb. 11 oz.
48 G 10218—White Crissy doll.............9.44
48 G 10219—Black Crissy doll.............9.44

Save 1.55. Crissy is only 7.89 when you buy her with stylish outfits, (9) below. Wt. 2 lbs. 2 oz.
48 G 10296—White Crissy with Outfits.....13.88
48 G 10294—Black Crissy with Outfits.....13.88

8 **Velvet with Swirly Daisies.** Lavender daisy chai swirls through Velvet's golden hair to creat exciting hair-do's whether her hair is long or shor braided, piled high or in a ponytail. For the coun try-look, she wears crisp plaid pinafore dres lavender like her daisies. About 15 in. tall. Ship wt. 1 lb. 11 oz.
48 G 10220—Velvet doll only...............9.4

Save 1.55. Velvet is only 7.89 when you buy her with pretty outfits, (10) below. Wt. 2 lbs. 2 oz.
48 G 10297—Velvet with Outfits............12.8

4 Outfits for Crissy **5⁹⁹** set

9 **Smart wardrobe for Crissy,** other 17½-18 in. fashion dolls. Stylish long skirt with blouse, lace-trimmed pj's, mint with stripe trim, layered-look pantsuit, apron. Colors, fabrics may vary.
48 G 11058—Outfits only. Ship. wt. 7 oz......5.99

4 Outfits for Velvet **4⁹⁹** set

10 **Latest styles for Velvet,** other 15-in. fashio dolls. Long skirt and body suit for evenings home, frilly pajamas, tunic with shorts, apror dressy pantsuit. Colors and fabrics may vary.
48 G 11059—Outfits only. Ship. wt. 7 oz.......4.9

The 1974 Wards catalog offers some clothes that fit Baby Crissy. They also sold some extra non-Ideal clothes for Crissy and Velvet, too.

"Ma"

1 $6.94

If someone keeps crying "Ma" for you, it just might be Baby Telefoam

(1) Baby Telefoam
Cries for "Ma" when you squeeze her arms, legs or body. You comfort her quiet again.
BODY, DETAILING: 16 in. tall. Soft vinyl body with polyurethane foam fill. Rooted hair. Painted eyes.
CLOTHES, ACCESSORIES: Dressed in blue, white checked dress with matching hat, pants. White socks.
FOR AGES: 3 to 8 years.
ORDERING INFORMATION:
49 C 31523—Shipping weight 1 lb. 12 oz. $6.94

(2) and (3) $11.94 each *without batteries*

2 **3** **4** 10-piece Wardrobe $3.99

Baby Come Back™ is already walking!
But she only goes a short way before coming back to you

(2 and 3) Baby Come Back™
Push her arms down and she toddles off, then walks back and lifts her arms to be picked up and loved.
BODY, DETAILING: 16 in. tall. Plastic body with jointed arms and legs. Rooted hair. Painted eyes.
CLOTHES, ACCESS.: Dress with matching shorts.
FOR AGES: 3 to 8 years.
ORDER INFO: Each requires 2 "C" batteries, not included, order package below. Shpg. wt. 2 lbs.
(2) 49 C 31581—Black Baby Come Back . . . $11.94
(3) 49 C 31578—White Baby Come Back . . . 11.94
Long-life Alkaline "C" Batteries. Package of 2.
49 C 46997—Shipping weight 5 ounces . . . . Pkg. $1.39
(4) 10-piece Wardrobe Set . . . for Baby Come Back. Includes 2-pc. playwear, dress and pants, 2-piece pajamas, comb and three plastic hangers.
ORDERING INFORMATION:
49 C 32527—Shipping weight 7 ounces . . . . . Set $3.99

DRINK 'N WET Infants
Give them a drink, change them, love them (5 thru 8) come with their own bottle

5 Asian look Baby $8.95

6 Black Baby $8.95

7 Hispanic look Baby $8.95

For (5 thru 7) Bottle, Comb, Brush Set

(5 thru 7) Cultural Little Friends
BODY, DETAIL: 13-in. high soft vinyl body, jointed arms, legs. Rooted hair. Painted eyes. Drinks, wets.
CLOTHES, ACCESS.: Doll outfit (as shown), plus bottle, comb, brush.
FOR AGES: 3 to 10 years. Not for ages under 3, due to small parts.
ORDERING INFO: Wt. 1 lb. 8 oz.
(5) Asian look Doll
49 C 31696 . . . . $8.95
(6) 49 C 31716—Black Doll . . . 8.95
(7) Hispanic look Doll
49 C 31688 . . . . 8.95

8 Doll and Layette $9.95

(8) Thirstee Baby with 8-pc. layette set
Drinks from life-size nursing bottle and wets.
BODY, DETAILING: 18 in. tall. Vinyl body with soft, vinyl jointed arms, legs. Rooted hair. Sleeping eyes.
CLOTHES, ACCESS.: Dressed in 1-pc. romper. Layette incl. quilted sleeping pad, terry cloth bib, diaper, pacifier, rattle, identification bracelet, birth announcement.
FOR AGES: 3 to 10. Not for under 3, due to small parts.
ORDERING INFORMATION:
49 C 31563—Shipping weight 2 lbs. 8 oz. $9.95

(9) Dampies® Drink 'n Wet Set
99c
Keep doll dry and comfy.
SET INCLUDES: 3 Dampies® play disposable diapers in their own box. Plastic nursing bottle.
FOR AGES: 4 years and up.
ORDER INFO: For dolls to 18 in.
49 C 32599—Wt. 7 oz. . . . . Set 99c

9 Dampies

Watch her hair "grow"

10 **11**

IDEAL 2-foot tall Baby Crissy
$18.97 each

(10 and 11) Baby Crissy
Pull her hair to make it "grow"; pull string on neck to shorten it.
BODY, DETAILING: 24 in. tall. Soft vinyl foam skin. Jointed arms, legs. Sparkling eyes.
CLOTHES, ACCESSORIES: Lavender dress and pants. Big enough to wear real baby clothes!
FOR AGES: 5 to 10 years.
ORDERING INFORMATION:
(10) White Crissy. Auburn hair.
79 C 31658C—Wt. 5 lbs. $18.97
(11) Black Crissy. Black hair.

Grown-up Candy Striper with medical supplies
BODY, DETAILING: 11 in. tall. Vinyl body with jointed arms and legs. Sleeping eyes. Long blond rooted hair.
CLOTHES, ACCESSORIES: Uniform and cap. Stethoscope, auriscope, box of bandages, thermometer, prescription pad, syringe, scissors, nurse's bag.
AGES: 3–10 yrs. Not recommended for ages under 3, due to small parts.
ORDERING INFORMATION:
49 C 32158—Wt. 1 lb. 8 oz. $7.99

NURSE BAG

FOLSOM Sears **453**

In 1977, Sears sold Baby Crissy for quite a hefty sum compared to the other dolls on this page. She is the only grow-hair girl offered in this catalog. Notice the white Baby is wearing black Baby's lavender outfit. Only now and then does she turn up wearing it today.

Chapter 12

Crissy's Fashion Show

Looking ultra-fashionable are Movin' Groovin' Crissy in "An Overall Effect" (1972) and Movin' Groovin' Velvet in "Cloud Movement" (1972).

Ready for a casual afternoon are Kerry in "Drenched Trench" (1971) and Crissy in "Jean Machine" (1971).

Top left: All dressed up in "Ocean Motion," "Checker Check," "On the Lamb," and "Blazering" (all 1972).

Bottom left: Looking crisp in "Skimmer" is a Look Around Crissy. She is enjoying the company of Cricket modeling "Blouson Battle" and Velvet in "Strawberry Smock" (all outfits, 1973). They are such a colorful trio!

"The Peace Poncho" (1970) has either a neon green T-shirt or a lemon yellow shirt trimmed with ric-rac. The peace sign necklace is plastic. The hair clip is from Montgomery Ward.

This "brown-haired Crissy" boldly steps out in "The Bold Blazer" (1969). The scarf fabric varies and is edge-finished with overlocking. There is a small brass ring used to cinch up the scarf around her neck. It is a hard-to-find outfit. (Box and outfit courtesy of Susan Mobley)

An unusual choice of attire for a pre-teen is the Sears exclusive Tressy wedding gown. She looks marvelous in it, as it contrasts so well with her raven black hair. Standing up for Tressy is Cricket in her bridesmaid's dress. The wrist corsage and the hair ornament varied greatly, as did the lace trim used on the dresses. This is a highly sought-after set by collectors when in prime condition.

Looking decidedly elegant in their formal wear are Brandi modeling "Hob Nobber" (1971) and Kerry in "Gypsy" (1971).

Top left: "Perfectly suited" Crissy and Velvet in "The Groovy Jumpsuit" (1969) and "Lace Pantsuit" (1970), respectively.

Bottom left: Two versions of "The City Pants Look": one is made of all-cotton woven fabrics; the other (right), of synthetic fabrics. The tie ring varies, as well.

These two are ready for a beach party. Brandi is wearing "Surf's Up" (1971). The bracelet with this outfit varies. Little Velvet looks cool in "Beachnik" (1971).

Top left: Looking sweet is a white Crissy in "Summer Social" (1973) and a black Swirla-Curler Crissy (1973) in "The Dreamer" (1973). They're pretty as a picture.

Bottom left: This colorful trio wears (left to right) "Glad Plaid" (1971), "Grape Drape" (1971), and "Kelly Coat" (1971).

All ready for a colorful summertime is Swirla-Curler Crissy wearing "Double Dip" (1973), and Mia looks great in "Smocked" (1973).

Top right: Looking perfect in pants: Velvet in "Playdots" (1971), Mia in "Ruffled Up" (1971), and Velvet in "Smarty Pants" (1971).

Bottom right: Kerry wears "Funderwear" (1971) and Crissy is modeling "The Snuggler" (1971). They look ready to relax.

These girls look extremely groovy in their clothes: "Funky Feathers," "Peasantries" (also known as "Loverly"), and "The Burlap Bag," all from 1972. The hair ornament in the Crissy doll's hair is from the Crissy Hair Styling set. The stick looks very much like a lollipop stick.

"Awesome!" is the only word to describe lovely Brandi in the hard-to-find "Blazering" outfit. ("Blazering" courtesy of Carolyn Burt.)

$30⁰⁰

Two summery Crissy dolls in "Lip Smackin' Good" and "Moonshine" (both 1972).

Top right: These three are dressed in primary colors: "Lemon Hang-up," "Patchworker," and "Superstars" (all 1972). "Patchworker" has a heart-shaped choker, not shown.

Bottom right: With so many clothing choices in 1972, it's difficult to make a decision! Velvet models "Dandy Denims." The mint-in-package outfits are "Kinky Kolors" (left) and "Shortcuts" (right).

Going out on the town when it's chilly requires coats like these: "Frontier Gear" and "Starshine" (both 1972).

Top right: This Cricket is modeling a non-Ideal outfit, but she looks very sweet in it. No doubt, she would look great in "Pulled Together" (1973), too. The "Pulled Together" outfit is somewhat hard to find.

Bottom right: This lovely Kerry doll models 1973's "Hippie Happening," an off-white peasant dress with yarn belt.

Markings

Not all markings are going to be consistent from Crissy® doll to Crissy doll or any other Ideal grow-hair issue. The collector will always find variations, even within a single issue. The Crissy doll's head was usually marked the same from year to year, but her body was always marked differently, sometimes within the same production year. However, for the most part, you will find the following to be true for most dolls within an issue name.

The marks on the first issues of Crissy (including the hair-to-her-feet, the hair-to-the-hips versions, and the 1970 issue in the aqua minidress) are found in two places, on her neck and on her derriere. On her neck it reads:

© 1968
IDEAL TOY CORP.
GH-17-H129

On her tush it reads:

© 1969
IDEAL TOY CORP.
GH-18
US. PAT. #3,162,976

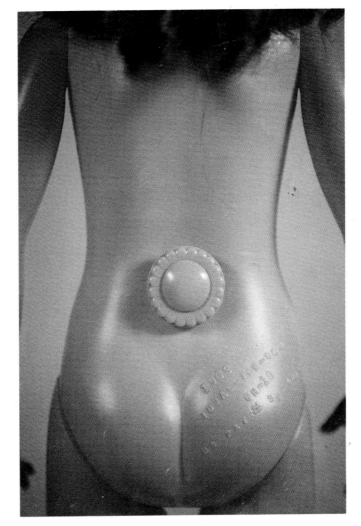

The easiest way to identify a Crissy is by her backside. This early doll has the flower-shaped knob and the early marks. There are no waist joints or pullstrings.

Movin' Groovin' Crissy has the same neck mark as the first-issue Crissy doll's, and has two body marks. One mark appears between her shoulder blades and reads:

© 1971
IDEAL.TOY.CORP.
MG-18
US. PAT. 3,162,976
OTHER PAT. PEND.

The Look Around Crissy doll's neck is also marked the same as the first issue's, with the addition of "HONG KONG," which is written above it. The marks between the shoulder blades read:

© 1972 IDEAL TOY CORP.
HONG KONG P.
U.S. PAT. NO 3, 162, 976
OTHER PATENTS PENDING

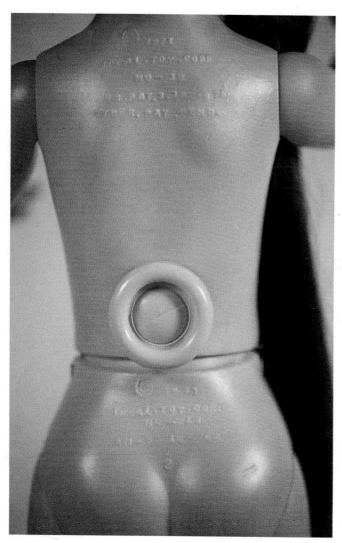

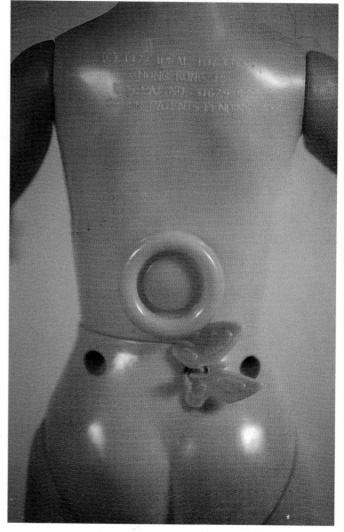

A Movin' Groovin' waist (also known as a Posin' waist on the Sears special dolls) has a joint that swivels. This doll also has the smooth, round knob. There is a rivet at each hip.

The Look Around Crissy body has a butterfly-shaped pullstring right under her knob. Two screw holes are rather obvious, too.

The markings on the Talky Crissy doll's neck are, again, the same as the first issue's. Her body markings are on her tush and read:

© 1970
IDEAL TOY CORP
U.S. PAT. 3,162,976
OTHER PAT. PEND.

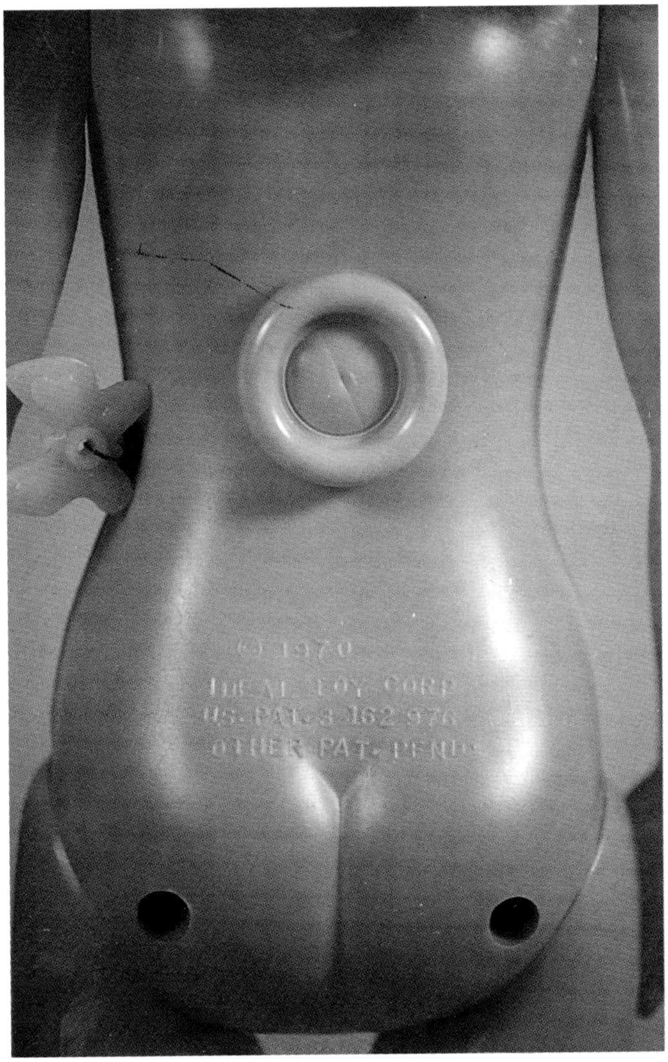

The Talky Crissy is identified by the butterfly-shaped pullstring on her left hip. There is no waist joint.

The markings on both the Swirla-Curler Crissy's and the Twirly Beads Crissy's heads are:

HONG KONG
© 1968
IDEAL TOY CORP.
GH-17-H129

Either above her grow-hair knob on her back, or else on the left cheek of her tush it may read "HONG KONG." On her right cheek, she has the same marks as the first-issue Crissy doll's.

Magic Hair Crissy has marks on her neck that read:

© 1977
IDEAL TOY CORP.
M.H.C.-19-H-281
HONG KONG

Her tush reads:

© 1974
IDEAL (in an oval)
HOLLIS, N.Y. 11423
2M-5854-01

The 1982-1983 Country Fashion Crissy and the 1982-1983 Beautiful Crissy made with the Velvet molds both have these markings on their necks:

73
©1969
IDEAL TOY CORP.
GH-15-H-157

Each of these issues also has this mark on her tush:

©1970
IDEAL TOY COR
GH-15
2M5169-01

Kerry has this mark on her neck:

©1970
IDEAL TOY CORP.
NGH-18-H-172
HONG KONG (sometimes)

The marks on her tush are the same as the number one Crissy doll's.

Tressy is marked as follows on the neck:

©1970
IDEAL TOY CORP.
SGH-17-H161
HONG KONG

The earlier 1970 Tressy is marked with the early Crissy doll's marks on the tush, and may or may not include the patent number. Posin' Tressy will have the Movin' Groovin' Crissy marks on the shoulder blades.

The markings that appear on Brandi's neck are:

©1971
IDEAL TOY CORP.
GHB-18-H-185
HONG KONG P

Her lower back reads:

©1971
IDEAL.TOY.CORP
MG-18
HONG.KONG.P

Velvet's head is marked:

©1969
IDEAL TOY CORP.
GH-15-H-157

The first Velvet's tushy reads:

©1970
IDEAL TOY CORP.
GH-15
169-01

or it may read:

©1970
IDEAL TOY CORP.
GH-15
2M5196-01
(sometimes 2M5169-01)

The Movin' Groovin' Velvet's head is marked the same as the first-issue Velvet's, but her tush is marked:

©1971
IDEAL TOY CORP.
M-15 (sometimes M-12)
2M-5217-02
1 (sometimes 2)

5317

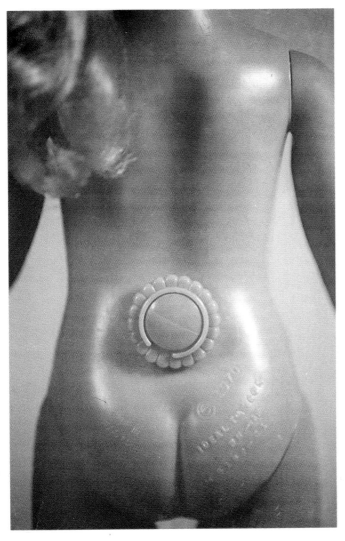

Early Velvet dolls have no waist joint. The marks are on the tushy as well as the neck.

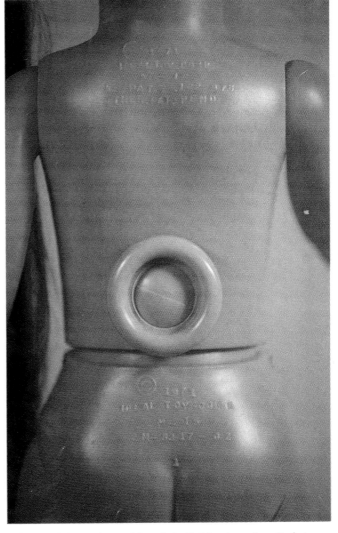

The Movin' Groovin' waist (also called a Posin' waist on Sears Exclusive dolls) has a swivel waist with rivets at hip.

Again, Talky Velvet's head is marked just like the first-issue Velvet's. Her marks on her lower back read:

©1971
IDEAL TOY CORP
TV15
US PAT 3 162 976
OTHER PATENTS PEND

Look Around Velvet's head is also marked in the customary manner. Her body marks appear between her shoulder blades and read as follows:

©1972
IDEAL TOY CORP.
HONG KONG P.
U.S. PAT. NO. 3.162.976
OTHER PATENTS PENDING

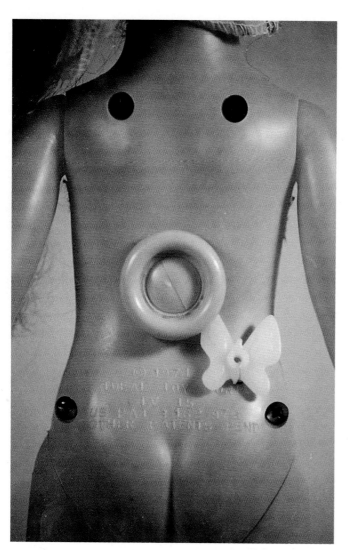

Talky Velvet has a butterfly pullstring under her knob. She has no waist joint.

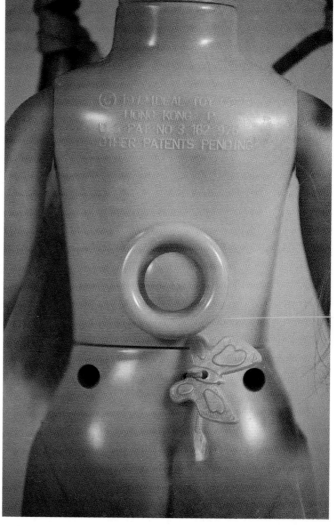

The Look Around Velvet waist is very similar to Look Around Crissy doll's waist with a butterfly pullstring under the knob.

Beauty Braider Velvet and Swirly Daisies Velvet can have either of the first two issues' body marks, and their neck markings are the same as the first-issue Velvet head mark.

The 1981-reissue Velvet's head is marked the same way as the first-issue Velvet's, and her tush has the mark:

©1970
IDEAL TOY COR
GH-15
2M5169-01 (this mark may vary)

Mia also has the early Velvet body mark cited above, as well as the following marks on her neck:

©1970
IDEAL TOY CORP.
NGH-15-H173

Cricket has these marks on her neck:

©1970
IDEAL TOY CORP.
CR-15-H-177
HONG KONG

Her tush reads:

©1971
IDEAL TOY CORP.
MG-15
HONG KONG P

Dina is marked on the neck:

©1971
IDEAL TOY CORP.
GHD-15-H-186
HONG KONG

Her tushy is printed with the same mark as Cricket's, as both have a posing waist.

Tara is marked on the neck:

©1975
IDEAL TOY CORP
H-250
HONG KONG

Her bottom is marked:

©1970
IDEAL TOY COR
GH-15
2M5169-01

The head mark for Velvet's Little Sister and all Cinnamon issues is:

©1971
IDEAL TOY CORP.
GH-12-H-188

On her shoulder blades it reads:

©1972
IDEAL TOY CORP.
U.S. PAT.3.162.976
OTHER PAT. PEND
HONG KONG P.

But, by 1974, some of the Curly Ribbons Cinnamons had
this on the shoulder blade:

> ©1972
> IDEAL TOY CORP.
> HONG KONG P.

Most Baby Crissy dolls (1970s and 1980s original molds)
were marked the same way. The head mark is:

> ©1972
> IDEAL TOY CORP.
> GHB-H-225

Markings on the doll's back read:

> ©1973
> IDEAL TOY CORP.
> GHB
> 2M-5611

The Crissy Price Guide

Crissy	MIB, all enclosures	Played with, in box	Dressed Doll	Nude
1969	$65-85	$50	$30	$20
1969, black	95-125	70-95	50	40
1970	65-85	50	30	20
1970 black	95-125	70-95	50	40
Movin' Groovin' ✦	65-85	50	30	20
MG, black	95-125	70-95	50	40
Talky	85-100	65	45	35
Look Around ✦	65-85	50	30	20
LA, black	95-125	70-95	50	40
Swirla-Curler	65-85	50	30	20
SC, black	95-125	70-95	50	40
Twirly Beads	65-85	50	30	20
TB, black	95-125	70-95	50	40
Magic Hair	60-70	45	25	15
MH, black	65-75	50	30	20
82, Country Fashion	60-70	45	25	15
82, CF, black	65-75	50	30	20
82 & 83, white dress	60-70	45	25	15
82 & 83, white dress, black	65-75	50	30	20

The Velvet Price Guide

Velvet	MIB, all enclosures	Played with, in box	Dressed Doll	Nude
1970	$60-75	$45	$25	$15
1970, black ✗	85-125	60-85	40	30
Movin' Groovin' ✗	60-75	45	25	15
MG, black	85-125	60-85	40	30
Talky	60-75	60	40	30
Look Around ✗	60-75	45	25	15
LA, black	85-125	60-85	40	30
Beauty Braider	60-75	45	25	15
BB, black	85-125	60-85	40	30
Swirly Daisies	60-75	45	25	15
SD, black	85-125	60-85	40	30
81, white dress ✗	55-65	40	20	10
81, wd, black	60-70	45	25	15

Crissy & Velvet's Friends Price Guide

Doll's Name	MIB, all enclosures	Played with, in box	Dressed Doll	Nude
Brandi	$65-75	$55-65	$25	$15
Cinnamon with Curly Ribbons	50-75	50	25	10
Cinnamon CR, black	125	100	60	15
Cinnamon with Hairdoodler	50-75	50	25	10
Cinnamon HD, black	125	100	60	15
Cricket	95-125	75-95	60	40
Dina	65-75	55-65	25	15
Kerry	65-75	55-65	25	15
Mia	65-75	55-65	25	15
Tara	125	100	60	40
Tressy	95-125	75-95	60	40
Tressy, black	125	100	60	40
Velvet's Little Sister	50-75	50	25	10

Baby Crissy Price Guide

Baby Crissy	MIB, head wrapped	Played with, in box	In original clothes	Nude
1973-1977	$65-95	$65	$50	$35
1973-1977, black	90-125	90	75	50
1981-1982	65-95	65	50	35
1981-1982, black	90-125	90	75	50
1984 (non-growing hair reissue)	25	20	15	10
1984, black (non-growing hair reissue)	30	25	20	15
1985 (non-growing hair reissue)	25	20	15	10
1985, black (non-growing hair reissue)	30	25	20	15
1991 reissue	25	20	15	10
1991, black	25	20	15	10
1991 Teeny Baby Crissy	15	10	5	n/a
1995 Beauty Parlor Baby Crissy	25	20	15	10
1995 BP Baby Crissy, black	25	20	15	10

Clothing Price Guide

Outfit	MIP, MIB	Loose/Complete
1969, "Groovy Jumpsuit"	$50	$25
1969 and 1970, "Turned On Mini"	50	25
1969, "Fun Fur Cape"	50	25
1969, "Bold Blazer"	50	25
1969 and 1970, "Sleeper Bells"	50	25
1969 and 1970, "City Pants Look"	50	25
1970, "Peace Poncho"	50	25
1970, "Seventies Satin"	50	25
1970, "With It Knit"	50	25
1970 Velvet, "Lavender School Girl Dress"	40	20
1970 Velvet, "Baby Doll PJs"	40	20
1970 Velvet, "Coat and Hat"	40	20
1970 Velvet, "Lace Pantsuit"	40	20
1971 Crissy, "Hob Nobber"	30	15
1971 Crissy, "Grape Drape"	30	15
1971 Crissy, "Surf's Up"	30	15
1971 Crissy, "Drenched Trench"	30	15

Outfit —	MIP, MIB	Loose/Complete
1971 Crissy, "Jean Machine"	$30	$15
1971 Crissy, "Gypsy"	30	15
1971 Crissy, "Snuggler"	30	15
1971 Crissy, "Funderwear"	30	15
1971 Velvet, "Kelly Coat"	25	12
1971 Velvet, "Glad Plaid"	25	12
1971 Velvet, "Beachnik"	25	12
1971 Velvet, "Ruffled Up"	25	12
1971 Velvet, "Play Dots"	25	12
1971 Velvet, "Smarty Pants"	25	12
1972 Crissy, "Lemon Lite"	50	25
1972 Crissy, "Feminine Fancy"	50	25
1972 Crissy, "Blazering"	50	25
1972 Crissy, "Very Vanilla"	50	25
1972 Velvet, "Checker Check"	30	15
1972 Velvet, "Ocean Motion"	30	15
1972 Velvet, "On the Lamb"	30	15

Clothing Price Guide cont ...

Outfit	MIP, MIB	Loose/Complete
1972 Velvet, "Blazering" (not Crissy's outfit of the same name)	$30	$15
1972 Crissy, "Patchworker"	30	15
1972 and 1973 Crissy, "Hippie Happening"	30	15
1972 Crissy, "Lip Smackin' Good"	30	15
1972 Crissy, "Starshine"	30	15
1972 Crissy, "Moonshine"	30	15
1972 and 1973 Crissy, "Funky Feathers"	30	15
1972 Crissy, "Burlap Bag"	30	15
1972 Crissy, "An Overall Effect"	30	15
1972 Velvet, "Super Stars"	25	12
1972 Velvet, "Cloud Movement"	25	12
1972 Velvet, "Kinky Kolors"	25	12
1972 and 1973 Velvet, "Peasantries" (or "Loverly")	25	12
1972 Velvet, "Shortcuts"	25	12
1972 and 1973 Velvet, "Dandy Denims"	25	12
1972 Velvet, "Frontier Gear"	25	12

Clothing Price Guide cont ...

Outfit	MIP, MIB	Loose/Complete
1972 Velvet, "Lemon Hang-Up"	$25	$12
1973 Crissy, "Summer Social"	30	15
1973 Crissy, "Double Dip"	30	15
1973 Crissy, "Skimmer"	30	15
1973 Crissy, "Dreamer"	30	15
1973 Velvet, "Blouson Battle"	25	12
1973 Velvet, "Strawberry Smock"	25	12
1973 Velvet, "Pulled Together"	25	12
1973 Velvet, "Smocked"	25	12
Crissy shoe pack	25	
Velvet shoe pack	25	
Crissy/Velvet boots, pair		10
Crissy Bow Flats or Mary Jane Wedgies, pair		8
Velvet T-strap shoes, pair		8
Crissy/Velvet Lace-Up Clogs, pair		8

Other Groovy Items Price Guide

Item	MIP, MIB	Loose/Complete
4-sided Tote for Beautiful Crissy, 1970	$30	$15
Hair Fashion Tote, 1970	40	20
4-sided Tote for Crissy/ Velvet Fashions, 1971	30	15
Miss Tressy Look-Alikes Wig	100	50
Miss Tressy Luggage, 1971 per piece	100	50
6-sided Crissy/Velvet Fashion Tote	50	25
6-sided Crissy and Friend Fashion Tote	50	25
Miss Crissy Luggage, per piece	75	40
Miss Velvet Luggage, per piece	75	40
Tressy and Cricket Steamer Trunk	75	40
Crissy and Velvet Steamer Trunk	75	40
Wardrobe	50	25
Beauty Parlor	50	25
Patterns	10 uncut	5 cut
1970 Crissy Paper Doll with wigs	20	10
1971 Boxed Beautiful Crissy Paper Doll	20	10

Item	MIP, MIB	Loose/Complete
1971 Crissy and Velvet Paper Dolls	$20	$10
1972 Boxed Crissy Paper Doll	20	10
1973 Crissy in Folder Paper Doll	20	10
Velvet & Crissy Shopping Spree Game	40	20
Crissy & Velvet Coloring Book	10	5
Crissy's Way-out Wig	50	25
Hair Care Set	50	25
Cases made by other manufacturers (not Ideal)	25	12
Outfits made by other manufacturers (not Ideal)	15	8

Checklist

Item	Price	Date Purchased	Comments
1969 Crissy, hair-to-floor			
1969 Crissy, black, h-t-f			
1969 Crissy, hair-to-hips			
1969 Crissy, black, h-t-h			
1970 Crissy			
1970 Crissy, black			
1971 Movin' Groovin' Crissy			
1971 MG Crissy, black			
1971 Talky Crissy			
1972-1973 Talky Crissy (same issue for both years)			
1972 Look Around Crissy			
1972 Look Around Crissy, black			
1973 Swirla-Curler Crissy			
1973 SC Crissy, black			
1974 Twirly Beads Crissy			
1974 TB Crissy, black			
1977 Magic Hair Crissy			
1977 MH Crissy, black			
1982 Country Fashion Crissy			
1982 CF Crissy, black			
1982-1983 Beautiful Crissy			
1982-1983 Beautiful Crissy, black			
1983 Country Fashion Crissy			
1983 CF Crissy, black			
1971 Kerry			
1970 Tressy, geometric print dress			

Checklist cont ...

Item	Price	Date Purchased	Comments
1971 Tressy, g. print dress, black			
1971 Posin' Tressy, aqua dress			
Tressy with bridal dress, gift set			
1972-1973 Brandi			
1970 Velvet			
1970 Velvet, black			
1971 Movin' Groovin' Velvet			
1971 MG Velvet, black			
1971 Talky Velvet			
1972-1973 Talky Velvet (same issue for both years)			
1972 Look Around Velvet			
1972 LA Velvet, black			
1973 Beauty Braider Velvet			
1973 BB Velvet, black			
1974 Swirly Daisies Velvet			
1974 SD Velvet, black			
1981 Velvet			
1981 Velvet, black			
1971 Mia			
1971 Posin' Cricket			
Cricket, bridesmaid's dress, gift set			
1972-1973 Dina			
1976 Tara			
1972 Velvet's Little Sister			
1973 Hairdoodler Cinnamon			
1973 HD Cinnamon, black			
1974 Curly Ribbons Cinnamon			
1974 CR Cinnamon, black			
Baby Crissy, pink diaper set			

Checklist cont …

Item	Price	Date Purchased	Comments
Baby Crissy, black, lavender diaper set			
1981-1982 Baby Crissy			
1981-1982 Baby Crissy, black			
Second 1982 Baby Crissy, in pink gingham			
Baby Crissy, pink gingham, black			
1984 Baby Crissy			
1984 Baby Crissy, black			
1985 Baby Crissy			
1985 Baby Crissy, black			
1991 Tyco Baby Crissy			
1991 Tyco Teeny Baby Crissy			
1991 Tyco Beauty Parlor Baby Crissy			
1969, "Groovy Jumpsuit"			
1969, "Turned On Mini"			
1969, "Fun Fur Cape"			
1969, "Bold Blazer"			
1969, "Sleeper Bells"			
1969, "City Pants Look"			
1970, "Peace Poncho"			
1970, "Seventies Satin"			
1970, "With It Knit"			
1970 Velvet, "Lavender School Girl Dress"			
1970 Velvet, "Baby Doll PJs"			
1970 Velvet, "Coat and Hat"			
1970 Velvet, "Lace Pantsuit"			
1971 Crissy, "Hob Nobber"			
1971 Crissy, "Grape Drape"			
1971 Crissy, "Surf's Up"			
1971 Crissy, "Drenched Trench"			

Checklist cont ...

Item	Price	Date Purchased	Comments
1971 Crissy, "Jean Machine"			
1971 Crissy, "Gypsy"			
1971 Crissy, "Snuggler"			
1971 Crissy, "Funderwear"			
1971 Velvet, "Kelly Coat"			
1971 Velvet, "Glad Plaid"			
1971 Velvet, "Beachnik"			
1971 Velvet, "Ruffled Up"			
1971 Velvet, "Play Dots"			
1971 Velvet, "Smarty Pants"			
1972 Crissy, "Lemon Lite"			
1972 Crissy, "Feminine Fancy"			
1972 Crissy, "Blazering"			
1972 Crissy, "Very Vanilla"			
1972 Velvet, "Checker Check"			
1972 Velvet, "Ocean Motion"			
1972 Velvet, "On the Lamb"			
1972 Velvet, "Blazering"			
1972 Crissy, "Patchworker"			
1972 Crissy, "Hippie Happening"			
1972 Crissy, "Lip Smackin' Good"			
1972 Crissy, "Starshine"			
1972 Crissy, "Moonshine"			
1972 Crissy, "Funky Feathers"			
1972 Crissy, "Burlap Bag"			
1972 Crissy, "An Overall Effect"			
1972 Velvet, "Superstars"			
1972 Velvet, "Cloud Movements"			
1972 Velvet, "Kinky Kolors"			

Checklist cont...

Item	Price	Date Purchased	Comments
1972 Velvet, "Peasantries" or "Loverly"			
1972 Velvet, "Shortcuts"			
1972 Velvet, "Dandy Denims"			
1972 Velvet, "Frontier Gear"			
1972 Velvet, "Lemon Hang-Up"			
1973 Crissy, "Summer Social"			
1973 Crissy, "Double Dip"			
1973 Crissy, "Skimmer"			
1973 Crissy, "Dreamer"			
1973 Velvet, "Blouson Battle"			
1973 Velvet, "Strawberry Smock"			
1973 Velvet, "Pulled Together"			
1973 Velvet, "Smocked"			
Tote for Beautiful Crissy and her Fashions			
Hair Fashion Tote			
Tote for Crissy & Velvet Fashions			
Miss Tressy Vanity Case			
Miss Tressy Shoulder Bag			
Miss Tressy Hat Box			
Miss Tressy Train Case			
Miss Tressy Look-Alikes Wig			
Crissy and Velvet 6-sided case			
Crissy & Friend Fashion Tote			
Miss Crissy Train Case			
Miss Crissy Shoulder Bag			
Miss Crissy Hat Box			
Miss Velvet Train Case			
Miss Velvet Shoulder Bag			
Miss Velvet Hat Box			
Tressy & Cricket Steamer Trunk			

Checklist cont ...

Item	Price	Date Purchased	Comments
Crissy & Velvet Steamer Trunk			
1971-1972 Wardrobe Set			
1973 Beauty Parlor			
Simplicity Patterns: #5276, Crissy			
#5276, Velvet			
#6061, Crissy			
#6061, Velvet			
#9138, Crissy			
#9138, Velvet			
#9698, Crissy			
#9698, Velvet			
#8519, Crissy only			
McCalls Pattern #2182, Crissy			
1970 Paper Dolls, Crissy w/wigs			
1971 Beautiful Crissy Paper Doll, boxed			
1971 Crissy & Velvet Paper Dolls			
1972 Crissy Magic Paper Doll, boxed			
1973 Crissy Paper Doll, folder			
Shopping Spree Game			
Crissy & Velvet coloring book			
Crissy's Way-out Wigs, brunette, afro			
Crissy's Way-out Wigs, blonde, afro			
Crissy's Way-out Wigs, brunette, layer cut			
Crissy's Way-out Wigs, blonde layer cut			
Crissy Poster			
1971-1973 Hair Care Set			
1971-1973 Hair Dryer			

Beth Gunther lives in the state of Georgia near Atlanta. She loves the Georgia climate and enjoys working in the front office of a large elementary school. She is married to Kent and has three children, Joshua Dutton, Shannon Dutton, and Miles Gunther. She also has one cat named Cricket (but not after Ideal's Cricket), a bird named Diego, two ducks, tons of fish, and other assorted animal life.

Besides writing for doll publications, the Crissy On-line newsletter and the *Chatty News* (a newsletter for Chatty Cathy doll collectors), Beth relaxes by replicating vintage doll clothes, making doll clothes from vintage patterns and vintage fabrics, surfing the net, photography, collecting Wade figurines, and being with friends and family. Always.

(J.B.J. 1994)